Math+

2nd Edition

Activity Book

Book Staff and Contributors

Tony Freedman   *Content Specialist*
Jennifer Marrewa, Jeff Pitcher   *Senior Instructional Designers*
Jay White   *Instructional Designer*
Jill Tunick   *Senior Text Editor*
Debra Foulks   *Text Editor*
Suzanne Montazer   *Creative Director, Print and ePublishing*
Carol Leigh   *Print Visual Designer*
Julie Jankowski   *Cover Designer*
Steve Mawyer   *Media Editor*
Amy Eward, David Stienecker   *Writers*
Amy Eward   *Senior Manager, Writers*
Susan Raley   *Senior Manager, Editors*
Luz Long   *Senior Project Manager*
Nols Myers   *Director K–8, Program Management*

Lynda Cloud   *Executive Vice President, Product Development*
David Pelizzari   *Vice President, K^{12} Content*
Kim Barcas   *Vice President, Creative*
Christopher Frescholtz   *Senior Director, Program Management*

Lisa Dimaio Iekel   *Director, Print Production and Manufacturing*

Illustrations Credits

All illustrations © K12 Inc. unless otherwise noted
Cover: Diver and turtle. © GoodOlga/iStockphoto.com

About K12 Inc.

K12 Inc., a technology-based education company, is the nation's leading provider of proprietary curriculum and online education programs to students in grades K–12. K^{12} provides its curriculum and academic services to online schools, traditional classrooms, blended school programs, and directly to families. K12 Inc. also operates the K^{12} International Academy, an accredited, diploma-granting online private school serving students worldwide. K^{12}'s mission is to provide any child the curriculum and tools to maximize success in life, regardless of geographic, financial, or demographic circumstances. K12 Inc. is accredited by CITA. More information can be found at www.K12.com.

ISBN: 978-1-60153-438-5   (online book)
ISBN: 978-1-60153-450-7   (printed book)
Printed by Quad Graphics, Versailles, KY, USA, April 2015

Contents

Applications of Operations

Lines, Angles, and Rotations

Fraction Sense

Measurement

Fraction Operations

Decimals and Equality with Fractions

Mathematical Reasoning

Geometry

Algebra Thinking

Perimeter and Area Formulas

Compare Area and Perimeter

Core Focus Multistep Area Story Problems

Numbers Through 1,000,000

Read and Write Numbers

Thousands					
hundred thousands	ten thousands	thousands	hundreds	tens	ones
5	2	8 ,	6	9	3

The standard form of the number is 528,693.
The word form is five hundred twenty-eight thousand, six hundred ninety-three.

Write the number in standard form.

1. three hundred ninety-two thousand, six hundred five

2. eight thousand, one hundred forty-three

3. nine hundred thirteen thousand

4. twenty-three thousand, eight hundred five

5. one hundred twenty-five thousand

Write the word form of the number.

6. 628,370   7. 9,009   8. 93,901

Read the number aloud.

9. 518,500   10. 69,700   11. 249,000

T R Y I T

Choose the word form of the number.

12. 601,490

    A. six hundred ten thousand, four hundred ninety

    B. six hundred thousand, one hundred ninety

    C. six hundred one thousand, four hundred ninety

    D. six hundred one thousand, four hundred nine

13. 237,730

    A. two hundred thirty-seven thousand, seven hundred thirty

    B. thirty-seven thousand, seven hundred thirty

    C. two hundred thirty-seven thousand, three hundred seventy

    D. two hundred thirty-seven thousand

14. 52,800

    A. fifty-two thousand, eighty

    B. fifty-two thousand, eight hundred

    C. five thousand, two hundred eighty

    D. five hundred twenty-eight thousand

15. Which of these word forms names the number 556,000?

    A. five hundred fifty-six thousand

    B. five hundred fifty-six

    C. five hundred fifty thousand, six hundred

    D. fifty-five thousand, six hundred

Read the story problem and follow the directions.

16. The moon is approximately three hundred eighty-four thousand, four hundred kilometers from the earth. Write this number in standard form.

17. There were four hundred forty thousand, three hundred twenty-one apples in the orchard's harvest. Write this number in standard form.

18. The seating capacity of the new Yankee Stadium is about fifty thousand, two hundred eighty-seven. Write this number in standard form.

19. Write this number in standard form: nine hundred thirty-one thousand, seventy.

TRY IT

Expanded Form Through 1,000,000

Numbers in Expanded Form

You can use a place-value chart to help you write numbers in expanded form two different ways.

PROBLEM Write the number 873,902 in expanded form two different ways—with words and numbers and with numbers only.

SOLUTION Show 873,902 in the place-value chart.

Thousands						
hundred thousands	ten thousands	thousands		hundreds	tens	ones
8	7	3	,	9	0	2

1. Line up the number 873,902 below the place-value chart.

2. Find the place-value position of each digit.

3. Write the digits followed by their place value in order from left to right across the page with + symbols between them.
   8 hundred thousands + 7 ten thousands + 3 thousands + 9 hundreds + 2 ones

4. Replace the word forms with the value of the digits.
   800,000 + 70,000 + 3,000 + 900 + 2

ANSWER 8 hundred thousands + 7 ten thousands + 3 thousands + 9 hundreds + 2 ones
800,000 + 70,000 + 3,000 + 900 + 2

Write the number in expanded form two different ways: (a) with words and numbers; (b) with numbers only.

1. 82,936

2. 120,398

3. 702,374

4. 346,007

LEARN

Worked Examples

You can use a place-value chart to help you write numbers in expanded form two different ways.

PROBLEM Write $800{,}000 + 30{,}000 + 900 + 90 + 6$ in standard form.

SOLUTION 1 Use a place-value chart. Write digits from the expanded number below their place value. If a place value is missing from the expanded form, write a 0 in that place-value position.

Thousands					
hundred thousands	ten thousands	thousands	hundreds	tens	ones
8	3	0	9	9	6

SOLUTION 2 Line up the numbers vertically and add.

$$
\begin{array}{r}
800{,}000 \\
30{,}000 \\
900 \\
90 \\
+\quad 6 \\
\hline
830{,}996
\end{array}
$$

ANSWER 830,996

Use your place-value chart to write the number in standard form.

5. $800{,}000 + 70{,}000 + 5{,}000 + 900 + 30 + 6$

6. 2 hundred thousands $+$ 6 thousands $+$ 8 hundreds $+$ 5 ones

7. 8 hundred thousands $+$ 7 ten thousands $+$ 6 thousands

8. $400{,}000 + 30{,}000 + 6{,}000 + 400 + 20 + 9$

LEARN

Expanded Form Through 1,000,000

Expanded Form

Memory Jogger

A place-value chart can help you locate the place-value position of each digit in a number so you can find the values of every digit. Then use the values to write the number in expanded form.

Thousands						
hundred thousands	ten thousands	thousands	,	hundreds	tens	ones

Choose the expanded form.

1. 123,300

   A. $100,000 + 2,000 + 300 + 30$

   B. $100,000 + 20,000 + 3,000 + 300$

   C. $10,000 + 2,000 + 300 + 30$

   D. $100,000 + 20,000 + 3,000 + 30$

2. 690,054

   A. $600,000 + 90,000 + 500 + 4$

   B. $600,000 + 9,000 + 50 + 4$

   C. $600,000 + 90,000 + 50 + 4$

   D. $600,000 + 90,000 + 500 + 40$

3. 281,000

   A. $200,000 + 80,000 + 1,000$

   B. $200,000 + 80,000 + 100$

   C. $200,000 + 8,000 + 100$

   D. $20,000 + 8,000 + 100$

TRY IT

4. 310,000

    A. 3 hundred thousands + 1 ten thousand

    B. 3 hundred thousands + 1 thousand

    C. 3 hundred thousands + 1 hundred

    D. 3 ten thousands + 1 thousand

Choose the standard form.

5. 300,000 + 60,000 + 500 + 40 + 2

    A. 365,042   B. 60,542   C. 365,420   D. 360,542

6. 4 hundred thousands + 6 ten thousands + 3 hundreds + 8 ones

    A. 460,308   B. 4,638,000   C. 463,008   D. 4,060,308

7. 2 hundred thousands + 4 ten thousands + 3 hundreds + 1 ten

    A. 240,310   B. 240,301   C. 204,310   D. 24,310

Write the standard form.

8. 200,000 + 8,000 + 9

9. 4 hundred thousands + 1 ten thousand + nine hundreds

Write the expanded form.

10. 784,893   **11.** 790,700

12. 809,060   **13.** 323,759

Write the number in expanded form with numbers only.

14. 834,000

15. 315,030

16. 432,650

TRY IT

Compare and Order Greater Numbers (A)

Comparing Numbers

Compare the numbers. Write $<$, $>$, or $=$.

1. 903,784 ☐ 912,081

2. 867,341 ☐ 1,000,000

3. 336,983 ☐ 334,883

4. 928,201 ☐ 928,201

5. 349,245 ☐ 294,365

6. 893,034 ☐ 893,078

Write a digit that makes the comparison sentence true.

7. 2☐3,809 $<$ 233,879

8. 529,087 $<$ ☐34,220

9. 891,☐98 $<$ 891,543

10. 346,487 $<$ 3☐7,269

11. 286,593 $<$ 2☐6,275 $<$ 297,801

Write the place-value position that you would use to decide which number is greater.

12. 349,333 $>$ 140,102

13. 893,998 $<$ 894,944

14. 874,983 $>$ 874,763

TRY IT

Compare the numbers and choose the answer.

15. 635,491 and 596,223

    A. $635,491 = 596,223$

    B. $635,491 > 596,223$

    C. $635,491 < 596,223$

16. 365,724 and 362,986

    A. $365,724 < 362,986$

    B. $365,724 = 362,986$

    C. $365,724 > 362,986$

17. 645,248 and 645,248

    A. $645,248 = 645,248$

    B. $645,248 < 645,248$

    C. $645,248 > 645,248$

18. 786,729 and 789,542

    A. $786,729 > 789,542$

    B. $786,729 < 789,542$

    C. $786,729 = 789,542$

19. 573,426 and 593,862

    A. $573,426 = 593,862$

    B. $573,426 > 593,862$

    C. $573,426 < 593,862$

20. 1,000,000 and 989,674

    A. $1,000,000 = 989,674$

    B. $1,000,000 > 989,674$

    C. $1,000,000 < 989,674$

TRY IT

Using Boundary Numbers for Rounding

Explain and Justify Rounding

Worked Examples

You can round a whole number by using a number line and by using place value.

PROBLEM 1 Round 325,737 to the nearest hundred thousand.

SOLUTION 1 Use a number line.

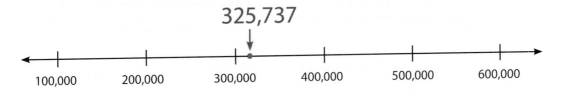

325,737

100,000   200,000   300,000   400,000   500,000   600,000

On the number line, 325,737 is closer to 300,000 than to 400,000.

SOLUTION 2 Use place value.

1 Underline the digit in the "rounding place," or the hundred thousands. Circle the digit in the place-value position to its right, in the ten thousands place.

Thousands				hundreds	tens	ones
hundred thousands	ten thousands	thousands		hundreds	tens	ones
<u>3</u>	(2)	5	,	7	3	7

2 If the circled digit is greater than or equal to 5, the digit in the rounding place increases by 1. To show its value, each digit to its right becomes 0.

The circled digit 2 is not greater than or equal to 5, so move to the next step.

3 If the circled digit is less than 5, the digit in the rounding place stays the same. To show its true value, each digit to its right becomes 0.

The circled digit $2 < 5$, so the 3 in the hundred thousands place stays the same. Each digit to its right becomes 0. So the rounded number is 300,000.

ANSWER To the nearest hundred thousand, 325,737 rounds to 300,000.

L E A R N

PROBLEM 2 Round 325,737 to the nearest ten thousand.

SOLUTION 1 Use a number line.

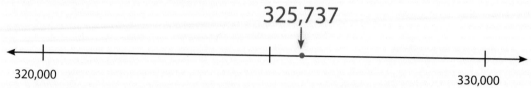

325,737

320,000   330,000

On the number line, 325,737 is closer to 330,000 than to 320,000.

SOLUTION 2 Use place value.

1 Underline the digit in the "rounding place," or the ten thousands.
Circle the digit in the place-value position to its right, in the thousands place.

Thousands					
hundred thousands	ten thousands	thousands	hundreds	tens	ones
3	2	5	7	3	7

2 If the circled digit is greater than or equal to 5, the digit in the rounding place increases by 1. To show its value, each digit to its right becomes 0.

The circled digit 5 = 5, so the 2 in the ten thousands place increases to 3, and each digit to its right becomes 0. So the rounded number is 330,000.

ANSWER To the nearest ten thousand, 325,737 rounds to 330,000.

Round each number and explain how you found your answer.

1. Round 620,751 to the nearest hundred thousand.

2. What is 627,137 rounded to the nearest ten thousand?

3. What is 62,500 rounded to the nearest thousand?

Round 471,453 to the nearest place value.

4. hundred thousand

5. ten thousand

6. thousand

7. hundred

Using Boundary Numbers for Rounding

Round Whole Numbers

Write the answer.

1. Round 486,751 to the nearest hundred thousand.

2. What is 469,218 rounded to the nearest ten thousand?

3. What is 12,500 rounded to the nearest thousand?

4. Redwood National Park contains 75,452 acres.
   Round this number to the nearest hundred.

5. What is 795,321 rounded to the nearest hundred thousand?

Round 394,329 to the nearest place value.

6. hundred thousand

7. ten thousand

8. thousand

9. hundred

10. ten

Choose the answer.

11. An airline reported that it flew 341,500 passengers in a one-month period.
    Which shows the number rounded to the nearest hundred thousand?

    A. 200,000

    B. 300,000

    C. 340,000

    D. 400,000

12. Which shows 917,652 rounded to the nearest thousand?

    A. 917,000

    B. 917,600

    C. 918,000

    D. 918,600

T R Y   I T

13. A reporter rounded the number of homes that were without power in Maine after a winter ice storm. The reporter said 250,000, which was correctly rounded to the nearest ten thousand. Which number could **not** be the number that was rounded?

A. 252,000

B. 250,925

C. 246,000

D. 243,000

14. Which shows 656,232 rounded to the nearest hundred thousand?

A. 700,000

B. 660,000

C. 600,000

D. 500,000

15. Round 481,594 to the nearest ten thousand.

A. 470,000

B. 480,000

C. 482,000

D. 490,000

16. Walter was asked to round a number to the nearest hundred thousand. He correctly wrote 500,000. Which number could be the number Walter was asked to round?

A. 548,661

B. 587,878

C. 578,900

D. 598,887

Read the problem and follow the directions.

17. Sandra wants to round 359,825 to the nearest ten thousand. Explain what she should do and write the correct answer.

18. Juliet wants to round 567,000 to the nearest hundred thousand. Explain what she should do and write the correct answer.

19. Taylor and Martha rounded the number 847,550 to the nearest thousand. Taylor said the answer is 848,000. Martha said the answer is 847,000. Who is correct? Explain.

20. Maya and Frankie rounded the number 24,317 to the nearest ten. Maya said the answer is 24,320. Frankie said the answer is 24,310. Who is correct?

21. A department store has donated school supplies to 107,547 schools for many years. Round this number to the nearest thousand.

TRY IT

Solve.

1. Rusty rounded 350,825 to the nearest hundred thousand and said it was 300,000. He rounded 350,825 to the nearest thousand and said it was 351,000. Was Rusty correct? Explain how you know.

2. Ticket sales show that 55,435 fans attended a concert on Friday night, and 54,675 fans attended on Saturday night. A news article about the concert said that about 55,000 fans attended the concert each night.

    (a) How could rounding explain why the reporter said the same number of fans attended each night?

    (b) Could the reporter use the same number of fans for each night if she rounded the numbers to the nearest ten thousand? Explain how you know.

3. Jupiter is the largest planet in our solar system. Jupiter's diameter at its equator is 142,984 kilometers.

    (a) What is Jupiter's diameter rounded to the nearest ten thousand kilometers? Explain how you know using place value.

    (b) What is Jupiter's diameter rounded to the nearest thousand kilometers? Explain how you know using place value.

    (c) Which rounded number would you use if you wanted to be more accurate? Why?

4. Julie makes jewelry out of beads. She has 17,892 clay beads and 12,321 glass beads.

    (a) Rounded to the nearest thousand, how many beads does Julie have in all? Explain how you know.

    (b) Rounded to the nearest hundred, how many beads does Julie have in all? Explain how you know.

    (c) Which number of beads is more accurate: the one rounded to the nearest thousand or the one rounded to the nearest hundred? Explain how you know.

TRY IT

Think Like a Mathematician Self-Check

5. State the actions and thinking you used during this lesson as a math learner.

Math Thinking and Actions
I made sense of problems by • Explaining to myself what a problem means and what it asks for • Using drawings or diagrams to represent a problem I was solving
I explained my math thinking clearly.
I tried out new ways to check if an answer is reasonable.
Other

TRY IT

Unit Review

Checkpoint Practice

Answer the question.

1. My number has a
    5 in the thousands place
    3 in the ten thousands place
    4 in the tens place
    2 in the hundreds place
    9 in the hundred thousands place
    6 in the ones place.
    What is my number?

2. The Great Lakes cover an area of 244,060 square kilometers. Round this number to the nearest ten thousand.

3. What is 95,321 rounded to the nearest thousand?

4. Write a number in the box to make this statement true.
    7 [?] 6,245 > 739,825

Choose the answer.

5. What is the value of 9 in the number 25,938?

    A. 90

    B. 900

    C. 9,000

    D. 90,000

6. Which number has a 7 in the hundred thousands place?

    A. 531,892

    B. 648,147

    C. 782,143

    D. 842,723

7. Which number means 700,000 + 60,000 + 1,000 + 200?

    A. 760,120

    B. 761,200

    C. 761,020

    D. 76,120

8. Which shows 803,700 written in expanded form?

    A. 800,000 + 30,000 + 700

    B. 800,000 + 3,000 + 70

    C. 800,000 + 3,000 + 700

    D. 800,000 + 30,000 + 7,000

UNIT REVIEW

9. Round 156,274 to the nearest hundred thousand.

   A. 100,000

   B. 150,000

   C. 200,000

   D. 260,000

10. Which means the same as 128,210?

    A. 1 hundred thousand + 2 ten thousands + 8 thousands + 2 thousands + 1 ten

    B. 1 hundred thousand + 2 ten thousands + 8 thousands + 2 hundreds + 1 ten

    C. 1 hundred thousand + 2 ten thousands + 8 ten thousands + 2 hundreds + 1 ten

    D. 1 ten thousand + 2 ten thousands + 8 thousands + 2 hundreds + 1 ten

11. Which shows 641,920 written in words?

    A. six hundred forty-one thousand, nine hundred twenty

    B. six hundred forty-one thousand, nine hundred two

    C. six hundred forty-one thousand, ninety-two

    D. sixty-four thousand, one hundred ninety-two

12. Which shows 423,920 written in words?

    A. four hundred twenty-three thousand, ninety-two

    B. four hundred twenty-three thousand, nine hundred twenty

    C. four hundred twenty thousand, three hundred ninety-two

    D. forty-two thousand, three hundred ninety-two

13. Which of these numbers is 830,300?

    A. eight hundred thousand, thirty-three

    B. eight hundred three thousand, three hundred

    C. eight hundred thirty thousand, three hundred

    D. eight hundred thirty thousand, thirty

Write in standard form.

14. four hundred forty-two thousand, seven hundred twenty-five

15. nine hundred twenty-two thousand, one hundred twenty-one

16. Mount McKinley in Alaska is twenty thousand, two hundred thirty-seven feet high.

17. The average person sleeps about one hundred ninety-four thousand, eight hundred twenty hours in a lifetime.

Choose the answer.

18. Mattie was asked to round a number to the nearest thousand. She correctly wrote 78,000. Which number could **not** be the number Mattie was asked to round?

   A. 78,115   B. 77,990

   C. 77,560   D. 77,269

19. Which set of numbers is in order from least to greatest?

   A. $373,926 < 374,794 < 374,852$

   B. $373,926 < 374,852 < 374,794$

   C. $374,852 < 373,926 < 374,794$

20. Joe wants to order the numbers 423,932; 395,632; and 428,765 from greatest to least. Which statement is correct?

   A. $423,932 > 395,687 > 428,765$

   B. $428,765 > 423,932 > 395,687$

   C. $395,687 > 428,765 > 423,932$

21. Compare the numbers 248,936 and 250,726 using $<$, $>$, or $=$.

   A. $248,936 = 250,726$

   B. $248,936 > 250,726$

   C. $248,936 < 250,726$

Answer the question.

22. What digit can replace the ? to make this comparison sentence true?
    $648,523 < 6\underline{\,?\,}9,246 < 658,523$

Estimate to Solve Problems (A)

Estimating Sums and Differences

Choose the best two numbers to use to estimate the sum or difference.

1. $293,345 + 467,982$
   A. 300,000
   B. 50,000
   C. 500,000
   D. 30,000

2. $524,345 + 398,352$
   A. 400,000
   B. 550,000
   C. 300,000
   D. 500,000

3. $56,903 - 30,452$
   A. 30,000
   B. 500,000
   C. 30,452
   D. 57,000

Use the compatible numbers from above to estimate the sum or difference. Use a number line if you wish.

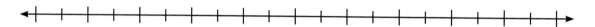

4. $293,345 + 467,982$

5. $524,345 + 398,352$

6. $56,903 - 30,452$

Use compatible numbers to estimate the sum or difference. Write the compatible numbers you used and your estimate.

7. $209,452 + 453,935$

8. $398,421 - 106,935$

9. $347,194 + 523,734$

Use compatible numbers to estimate and solve the problem.

10. There were 20,208 people at the soccer stadium before the game started. Another 12,962 people came into the stadium after the game started. About how many people were at the stadium in total? Remember, one way to find compatible numbers is to round. Round the numbers to the nearest thousand.

TRY IT

Solve using compatible numbers. Choose the best answer.

11. There were 2,598 people in the amusement park before 9:30 a.m. Another 824 people entered the amusement park between 9:30 and 10:30 a.m.

Which number sentence best shows the estimate of the total number of people at the park at 10:30 a.m.?

A. $2,000 + 800 = 2800$

B. $2,500 + 800 = 3,300$

C. $2,600 + 800 = 3,400$

D. $3,000 + 800 = 3,800$

12. Star Theaters made $21,283 on Friday and $58,678 on Saturday. About how much more did Star Theaters make on Saturday than on Friday?

Which number sentence best shows this estimate?

A. $\$59,000 - \$30,000 = \$29,000$

B. $\$58,678 - \$21,000 = \$37,678$

C. $\$58,000 - \$20,000 = \$38,000$

D. $\$60,000 - \$20,000 = \$40,000$

T R Y   I T

Estimate to Solve Problems (B)

Estimate to Solve Problems

Use compatible numbers to estimate the sum or difference of the equation. Try rounding to the nearest thousand, ten thousand, or hundred thousand to find the compatible numbers. Find the value of the variable, represented by a letter.

1. $78,340 - 45,300 = x$

2. $193,392 + 54,698 = b$

3. $394,394 + 108,399 = m$

4. $6,944 - 3,298 = w$

Use the compatible numbers to solve the problem. Round to the nearest thousand to find the compatible numbers.

5. The Mauna Kea volcano in Hawaii is 33,504 feet tall from the ocean floor to its peak. The Aloha peak is 1,206 feet tall. Use compatible numbers to estimate about how much taller the Mauna Kea peak is than the Aloha peak.

6. The Yosemite Falls are 2,425 feet tall. The Shannon Falls are 1,105 feet tall. Use compatible numbers to estimate about how much taller the Yosemite Falls are than the Shannon Falls.

7. A group of climbers were climbing Mount Kilimanjaro. The first week, they climbed 7,076 feet. The second week, they climbed another 8,923 feet. How many total feet did they climb in 2 weeks?

TRY IT

Solve. Support your solution with equations.

8. In January 2013, there were 112,802 visitors to the Kona side of the Big Island of Hawaii. In that same month, there were 48,606 visitors on the Hilo side. On the island of Kaua'i, there were 92,142 visitors. About how many more people visited the Big Island than Kaua'i?

9. In February, 2014, Yosemite National Park had 152,954 total visitors, the Grand Canyon had 178,887 total visitors, and Mount Rushmore had 62,513 total visitors. Estimate how many more visitors there were to Yosemite and Mount Rushmore than there were to the Grand Canyon.

10. The total earnings for an amusement park in January, February, and March were about $996,000. In January, the park earned $228,705. In February, it earned $491,923. About how much money did the amusement park earn in March?

TRY IT

Multiply Multidigit Numbers (A)

Multiplication Statements and Equations

Worked Examples

You can use number lines to help you understand equations involving multiplication.

PROBLEM 1 Use a number line to write the equation $35 = 5 \times 7$ as a comparison statement.

SOLUTION

1 Mark 0 on the number line toward the left side. Then label the first tick mark to the right of 0 with 7. Label the next tick mark with 14. Keep labeling, adding 7 to each previous label, ending with 35. Your number line should look similar to this one:

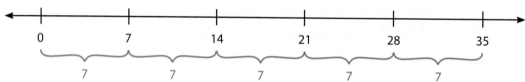

2 View the number line as showing that 35 is 5 groups of 7. In slightly different words, 35 is 5 times as many as 7.

ANSWER 35 is 5 times as many as 7.

PROBLEM 2 Write an equation for the statement:

54 is 9 times as many as 6.

SOLUTION

1 Use a number line to help you visualize this statement.

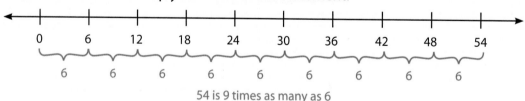

54 is 9 times as many as 6

2 Write the equation: $54 = 9 \times 6$.

ANSWER $54 = 9 \times 6$

LEARN

Interpret the equation as a comparison statement. Use a number line to help, if necessary.

1. $42 = 6 \times 7$

2. $32 = 8 \times 4$

3. $50 = 10 \times 5$

4. $72 = 6 \times 12$

Write the comparison statement as an equation.

5. 28 is 4 times as many as 7.

6. 36 is 4 times as many as 9.

7. 20 is 10 times as many as 2.

8. 49 is 7 times as many as 7.

LEARN

Multiply Multidigit Numbers (A)

Multidigit Multiplication

FINDING A PRODUCT Use partial products to make multiplying multidigit numbers easier.

$$225 \times 5$$

1 Rewrite the multiplication sentence so that each value in the multidigit number is multiplied by the one-digit number.

$$200 \times 5 + 20 \times 5 + 5 \times 5$$

2 Find the product of each part.

$$1,000 + 100 + 25$$

3 Add the partial products.

$$1,125$$

$$225 \times 5 = 1,125$$

Find the product.

1.
$$\begin{array}{r} 328 \\ \times\ \ 6 \\ \hline \end{array}$$

2.
$$\begin{array}{r} 692 \\ \times\ \ 5 \\ \hline \end{array}$$

3.
$$\begin{array}{r} 216 \\ \times\ \ 4 \\ \hline \end{array}$$

4. $5,876 \times 5$

$$\begin{array}{r} 5,876 \\ \times\ \ \ \ 5 \\ \hline \end{array}$$

5.
$$\begin{array}{r} 2,983 \\ \times\ \ \ \ 7 \\ \hline \end{array}$$

6. $4,339 \times 8$

$$\begin{array}{r} 4,339 \\ \times\ \ \ \ 8 \\ \hline \end{array}$$

TRY IT

24

Explain how to solve the problem.

7. Multiply 5,809 × 4.

Write an equation to represent the statement.

8. 56 is 8 times as many as 7.

Solve.

9. Party Décor sells crates of 462 paper plates.
How many individual paper plates are there in 9 crates?

TRY IT

Multiply Multidigit Numbers (B)

Practice 2-Digit Multiplication

Find the product.

1. Multiply 95 by 32.

$$\begin{array}{r} 95 \\ \times\ 32 \\ \hline \end{array}$$

2. Multiply 16 by 14.

$$\begin{array}{r} 16 \\ \times\ 14 \\ \hline \end{array}$$

3. Multiply 42 by 36.

$$\begin{array}{r} 42 \\ \times\ 36 \\ \hline \end{array}$$

4. Multiply 39 by 21.

$$\begin{array}{r} 39 \\ \times\ 21 \\ \hline \end{array}$$

Explain how to solve the problem.

5. Multiply 12 by 17.

6. Multiply 57 by 48.

TRY IT

Choose the number sentence that solves the problem.

7. One month Yolanda planted 24 flowers. The next month her sister planted 12 times as many flowers. How many flowers did Yolanda's sister plant?

   A. $24 \div 12 = 2$

   B. $24 + 12 = 36$

   C. $24 \times 12 = 288$

   D. $24 - 12 = 12$

8. Jenna played in 24 basketball games. At each game she scored 12 points. How many points did Jenn score in all?

   A. $24 \times 12 = 248$

   B. $24 \times 12 = 288$

   C. $24 \times 12 = 296$

   D. $24 \times 12 = 396$

TRY IT

Area Models for Multiplication (A)

Model Multiplication Comparisons

Worked Examples

You can use a tape diagram to model and solve multiplication problems.

PROBLEM 1 Use a tape diagram to represent the problem. Then solve.

Jenny is 7 years old. Mike is 3 times the age of Jenny. How old is Mike?

$7 \times 3 = M$ M is Mike's age.

SOLUTION Jenny's age:

7

Mike's age (3 times as many as Jenny's age):

7	7	7

$7 \times 3 = 21$

ANSWER Mike is 21 years old.

PROBLEM 2 Write equations to show the problem. Use a letter, or variable, to represent the unknown value. Then solve.

A green ribbon is 5 inches long. A blue ribbon is 6 times as long as the green ribbon is. How long is the blue ribbon?

G is the length of the green ribbon, or 5 inches.

B is the length of the blue ribbon, the unknown amount.

$G \times 6 = B$

SOLUTION $G \times 6 = B$

$5 \times 6 = 30$

5

5	5	5	5	5	5

ANSWER $B = 30$ The blue ribbon is 30 inches long.

LEARN

Solve. Draw a tape diagram to represent the problem.

1. A salad costs $2. A salmon dinner costs 5 times as much. How much does the salmon dinner cost?

2. The width of a garden is 6 feet. The length is 3 times the width. What is the length of the garden?

3. A small picture frame costs $3. A larger picture frame costs 9 times as much. How much does the larger frame cost?

Write an equation to describe the problem. Use letters to represent both the known and the unknown quantity.

4. Brian is 8 years old. His dad, Lenny, is 4 times as old as Brian is. How old is Lenny?

5. Samantha is 14 years old. Her aunt is 3 times as old as Samantha is. How old is Samantha's aunt?

6. On Tuesday, Julia jogged 12 miles. On Wednesday, she jogged 2 times the distance she jogged on Tuesday. How many miles did Julia jog on Wednesday?

7. Marisol bought a dress for $13. Her sister, Dina, bought a dress that cost 5 times as much. How much did Dina's dress cost?

Solve for the unknown quantity in the problem.

8. Samantha is 14 years old. Her aunt is 3 times as old as Samantha is. How old is Samantha's aunt?

9. On Tuesday, Julia jogged 12 miles. On Wednesday, she jogged 2 times the distance she jogged on Tuesday. How many miles did Julia jog on Wednesday?

10. Marisol bought a dress for $13. Her sister, Dina, bought a dress that cost 5 times as much. How much did Dina's dress cost?

LEARN

Area Models for Multiplication (A)

Area Models

Multiply.

1. $2 \times 18 = \square$

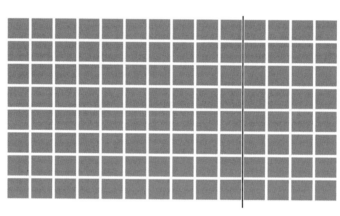

2. $3 \times 19 = \square$

3. $14 \times 8 = \square$

4. $16 \times 7 = \square$

Use grid paper to show how to solve the problem.

5. $16 \times 8 = \square$

6. $17 \times 5 = \square$

TRY IT

Choose the answer.

7. Which shows $114 \times 5 = \square$?

A.
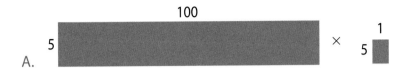

B.

C. 5 [100] + 5 [10] + 5 [4]

D. 114 × 114 × 114 × 114 × 114

TRY IT

Area Models for Multiplication (B)

Solve with Area Models

Answer the question.

1. Which model shows $17 \times 14 = \square$? Choose the answer.

A.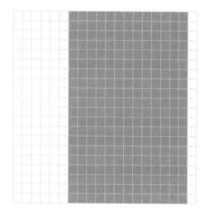

B.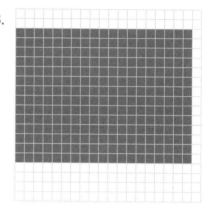

C.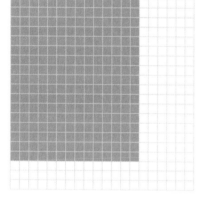

2. What is the product of $17 \times 14 = \square$?

3. Show 23×15 with an area model on grid paper.

4. How can you use the area model to find the product of 23×15?

TRY IT

Multiply. Use grid paper to help you make area models for each equation.

5. $15 \times 24 = \boxed{}$

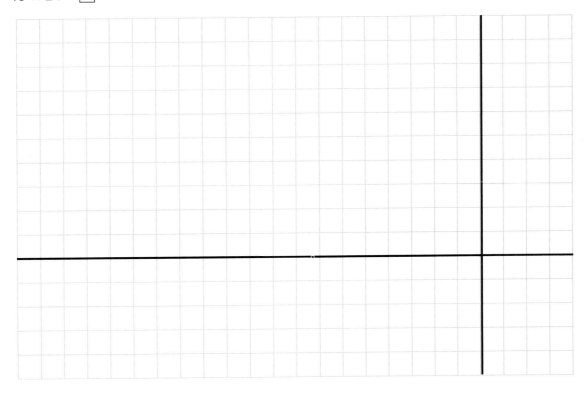

6. $23 \times 34 = \boxed{}$

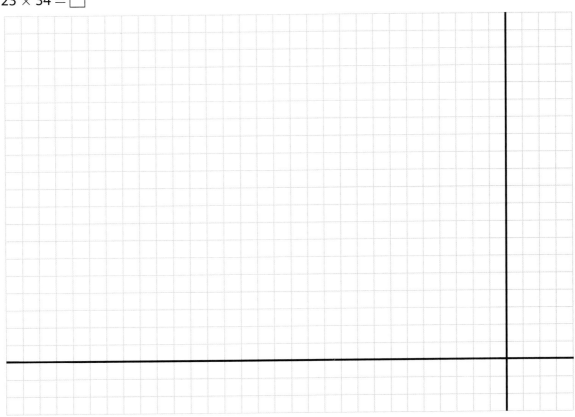

TRY IT

Multiply 4-Digit Numbers by 1-Digit Numbers

Use Partial Products to Multiply

Memory Jogger

MULTIPLYING A MULTIDIGIT NUMBER BY A ONE-DIGIT NUMBER USING PARTIAL PRODUCTS

1 Rewrite the multidigit factor in expanded form.

2 Multiply each part of the multidigit factor by the second one-digit factor.

3 Add the partial products.

Rewrite the multidigit factor in expanded form.

1. 3,678

2. 4,509

Multiply using partial products. Show your work.

3. $3,678 \times 3 =$ ___?___

4. $4,509 \times 4 =$ ___?___

Multiply. Use either partial products or the standard algorithm for multiplication.

5. $7,213 \times 8$

6. $5,059 \times 3$

7. $2,992 \times 7$

8. $6,741 \times 6$

TRY IT

Multiply Two 2-Digit Numbers

2-Digit Multiplication

Memory Jogger

FINDING A PRODUCT Use place value to make multiplying two-digit numbers easier.

1 Multiply the value of the ones digit of the second number by the values of the ones and tens digits of the first number.

2 Multiply the value of the tens digit of the second number by the values of the ones and tens digits of the first number.

3 Add the partial products to find the final product.

Find the product.

1. Multiply 84 by 16.

$$\begin{array}{r} 84 \\ \times\ 16 \\ \hline \end{array}$$

2. Multiply 26 by 24.

$$\begin{array}{r} 26 \\ \times\ 24 \\ \hline \end{array}$$

3. Multiply 52 by 26.

$$\begin{array}{r} 52 \\ \times\ 26 \\ \hline \end{array}$$

4. Multiply 19 by 61.

$$\begin{array}{r} 19 \\ \times\ 61 \\ \hline \end{array}$$

Explain how to solve the problem.

5. Multiply 14 by 19.

6. Multiply 51 by 27.

TRY IT

Choose the number sentence that solves the problem.

7. One month Northside Park planted 48 flowers. The next month Southside Park planted 12 times as many flowers. How many flowers did Southside Park plant?

   A. $48 \div 12 = 4$

   B. $48 + 12 = 60$

   C. $48 \times 12 = 576$

   D. $48 - 12 = 36$

8. Cally bought 15 crates of water. Each crate has 24 bottles of water. How many total bottles of water did Cally buy?

   A. $15 \times 24 = 360$

   B. $15 \times 24 = 380$

   C. $15 \times 24 = 460$

   D. $15 \times 24 = 480$

TRY IT

Model and Explain Division

Represent Division Problems

Use color tiles to solve.

1. $48 \div 6 = \underline{?}$

2. $36 \div 9 = \underline{?}$

3. $35 \div 7 = \underline{?}$

4. $\underline{?} = 28 \div 7$

5. $\underline{?} = 18 \div 3$

6. $20 \div 4 = \underline{?}$

7. Kristina has 18 grapes.
   She wants to give 2 grapes to each person.

   How many people can she give grapes to?

8. Mark has 40 tiles.
   He wants to put 4 tiles onto each tray.

   How many trays will Mark need?

9. Johnny has a bag of 36 cat treats. He gives 3 treats to each cat.

   How many cats are there?

10. Which sketch shows $15 \div 3 = ?$

A.
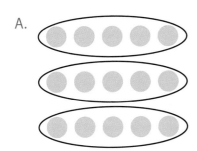

B.
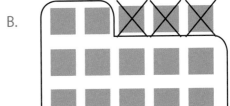

C.

D.
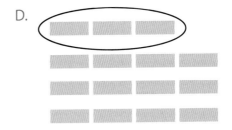

TRY IT

Division as Sharing

Equal Sharing

You can think of division as equal sharing.

PROBLEM 1 There are 84 campers going on a field trip. An equal number of campers will ride each of 4 shuttle buses. How many campers will ride each bus?

SOLUTION The campers are being shared equally among the 4 buses: each bus will have an equal number of campers.

1 Write a division equation to represent the problem: $84 \div 4 = c$.

2 Use base-10 blocks to show the 84 campers. Draw 4 rectangles to represent the 4 buses.

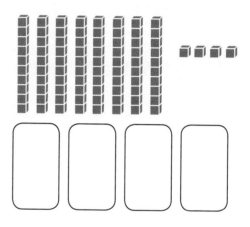

3 Share the base-10 blocks equally among the 4 rectangles. Place a tens rod in each rectangle until there are no more tens rods.

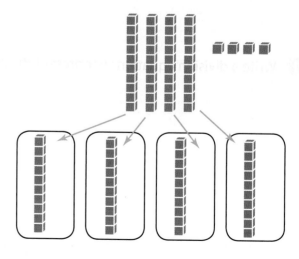

Place a ones cube in each rectangle until there are no more ones cubes.

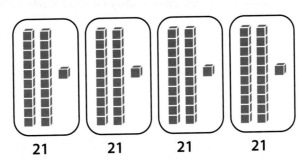

4 Count the base-10 blocks in each group.

21   21   21   21

ANSWER $84 \div 4 = c$

$84 \div 4 = 21$

Each shuttle bus will seat 21 campers.

PROBLEM 2 Lina picked 72 cherries. She divides them equally into 3 bags. How many cherries are in each bag?

SOLUTION The cherries are being shared equally among the 3 bags. Each bag will have an equal number of cherries.

1 Write a division equation to represent the problem: $72 \div 3 = c$.

2 Use base-10 blocks to show the 72 cherries. Draw 3 circles to represent the 3 bags.

3 Share the base-10 blocks equally among the 3 circles.

Begin by placing a tens rod in each circle. After placing 6 tens rods, 1 tens rod remains. Trade the tens rod for 10 ones cubes.

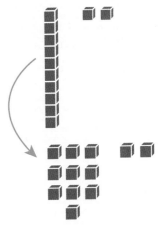

Place a ones cubes in each circle until there are no more ones cubes.

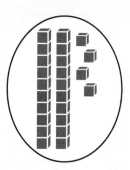 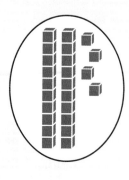 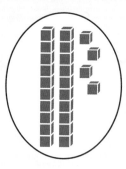

4 Count the base-10 blocks in each group.

ANSWER $72 \div 3 = c$

$72 \div 3 = 24$

There are 24 cherries in each bag.

Solve.

1. Malcolm has to read 96 pages over 4 days. He decides to read the same number of pages each day.

   (a) Write an equation to model the story problem. Use a letter to represent the unknown amount.

   (b) How many pages does Malcolm read each day? Explain your answer using base-10 blocks.

2. Dina has 85 books to place on 5 shelves. She wants to place an equal number of books on each shelf. How many books should she place on each shelf? Explain how you solved the problem.

Division as Sharing

Explain Division

Use base-10 blocks to show how to solve the problem.
Give your answer.

1. Aisha wanted to put 72 muffins in boxes. She could put 6 muffins in each box. How many boxes would she need?

2. Destiny wanted to put 39 baseballs in 3 bags. If she put the same number of baseballs in each bag, how many baseballs would she put in each bag?

3. Julianne has 75 marbles to share with 5 people. She wants to give each person the same number of marbles. How many marbles will each person get?

4. Frankie has 36 carrot sticks to share with 4 people. He wants to give each person the same number of carrot sticks. How many carrot sticks will each person get?

Choose the answer.

5. Beverly wanted to solve this problem. Thirty avocado trees were planted in 5 rows. There were the same number of trees in each row. How many trees were planted in each row?

Which shows a correct way to solve this problem?

A.

6 trees in each row

B.

5 trees in each row

C.

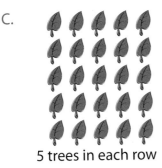

5 trees in each row

D.

10 trees in each row

TRY IT

Choose the answer.

6. Maria wanted to solve this problem. The band director wants his band marching in 3 equal columns. If there are 24 members in the band, how many will be in each column?

   Which shows a correct way to solve this problem?

   A.

   3 band members in each column

   B.

   4 band members in each column

   C.

   8 band members in each column

   D.

   6 band members in each column

TRY IT

Dividing with Remainders

Divide with Leftovers

Worked Examples

You can use objects in the problem or sketches to solve division story problems in which the objects in the problem do not divide evenly. What you do with the amount left over depends on what the story problem asks.

PROBLEM 1   A baker has 23 muffins and wants to place 4 in each box. How many boxes of 4 can the baker completely fill?

SOLUTION $23 \div 4 = ?$

Use 2 tens rods and 3 ones cubes to show the 23 muffins. Begin by dividing the tens into 4 equal groups. Since there are only 2 tens rods, trade the 2 tens rods for 10 ones cubes each. Now divide the ones cubes. You will have 5 complete groups and 3 muffins left over.

$23 \div 4 = 5\ r\ 3$

Since the question asked how many boxes of 4 the baker can completely fill, the answer is 5. Ignore the 3 muffins left over.

ANSWER   The baker can completely fill 5 boxes.

PROBLEM 2   A baker has 23 muffins and wants to place 4 in each box. How many muffins will be left over after he fills as many boxes of 4 as he can with the muffins?

SOLUTION $23 \div 4 = ?$

Since the question asked how many muffins will be left over, the answer is 3.

$23 \div 4 = 5\ r\ 3$

ANSWER   There will be 3 muffins left over.

L E A R N

PROBLEM 3 A baker has 23 muffins and wants to place 4 in each box. How many boxes does he need if he is selling all 23 muffins?

SOLUTION $23 \div 4 = ?$

Since the baker wants to sell all the muffins, he needs 5 boxes for the complete groups and a sixth box for the leftover muffins.

$23 \div 4 = 5 \, r \, 3$

ANSWER The baker needs 6 boxes.

Use base-10 blocks to solve.

1. The circus clown wants to share 20 balloons among 3 children. How many balloons would each child get?

   (a) How do you write the problem?

   (b) What should you do with the remainder?

   (c) What is the answer?

2. The bakery donated 23 pies to the children's band to serve at the parties after shows. If there are 2 shows, how many pies will be served after each show?

   (a) How do you write the problem?

   (b) What is the answer?

3. The scout leader is renting buses to take 35 campers to the campsite. Each bus holds 10 campers. How many buses should the scout leader rent to take everyone on the camping trip?

   (a) How do you write the problem?

   (b) What should you do with the remainder?

   (c) What is the answer?

4. Mr. Baker is arranging 45 muffins with 7 on each plate to take to the community breakfast. He decides that if there are any muffins left over, he will give them to his children. Will his children get any muffins? If they will, how many muffins will they get?

   (a) How do you write the problem?

   (b) What should you do with the remainder?

   (c) What is the answer?

Solve

5. The chef has 15 sandwiches to separate equally on 3 platters. How many sandwiches will go on each platter?

6. There are 28 marbles in a bag. Each player needs 5 marbles to play a game. How many players can play?

7. The kennel has 26 doggie treats for 10 dogs to share evenly. The leftovers will be placed back in the jar. How many treats will go back in the jar?

Dividing with Remainders

Division Story Problems

Solve. Use base-10 blocks to help you. Be sure to use the remainder correctly.

1. There are 38 slices of watermelon to separate equally on 9 plates. How many slices of watermelon will be on each plate? How many slices will be left over?

2. Sally found 42 shells at the beach. She wants to put exactly 5 shells into each bucket. How many buckets will have 5 shells?

3. Gordon has 74 grapes for his 6 friends. He wants to give each person the same number of grapes. How many grapes will each friend get?

4. Joel has 42 beads. He wants to sew 8 beads onto each shirt. After using all of the beads, how many will be left over?

TRY IT

Divide Greater Numbers

Model and Record Multidigit Division

Worked Examples

You can use base-10 blocks to understand the standard algorithm for division.

PROBLEM $2\overline{)926}$

SOLUTION

1   Write the problem on the Long Division – Hundreds printout.

2   Start with the hundreds. Underline the 9. Divide the 9 hundreds flats evenly into 2 groups. There are 4 hundreds flats in each group. Write a 4 in the hundreds place of the quotient over the 9 to show that you put 4 hundreds in each group.

3   Think, "4 hundreds times 2 is 8 hundreds, so 800 of the 926 blocks have been divided up." Subtract 800 from 926; there are 126 blocks left to divide.

4   Write 800 under 926 on the printout. Also write a minus symbol. Subtract.

$400 \times 2 = 800$

5   Think, "There are 126 blocks left to divide. Of that, there is 1 hundred. I can't put 1 hundred into 2 groups, so I have to break it into tens." Regroup the hundreds flat into 10 tens rods. Add those to the 2 tens you already have; that makes 12 tens.

6   Underline the 12 tens. Divide 12 tens by 2. The answer is 6 tens. Write a 6 in the tens place of the quotient on the printout.

7   Think, "6 tens times 2 is 12 tens or 60 times 2 equals 120," so you've divided up 120 more of out 926. Write 120 under the 126 on your printout. Subtract.

$400 \times 2 = 800$

$60 \times 2 = 120$

L E A R N

(8) See that there are 6 ones left to divide. Divide the ones cubes into 2 groups. There are 3 in each group. Record the 3 in the ones column of the quotient. Think, "3 ones times 2 is 6 ones." Write 6 in the ones column under the 6 at the bottom. Subtract to get zero; this shows you've divided up all the blocks. You can say this problem as "926 divided by 2 equals 463."

Hundreds	Tens	Ones	
4	6	3	

$$2\overline{)9\ 2\ 6}$$
$$-\ 8\ 0\ 0 \qquad 400 \times 2 = 800$$
$$\quad\ 1\ 2\ 6$$
$$-\ 1\ 2\ 0 \qquad 60 \times 2 = 120$$
$$\qquad\quad 6$$
$$\qquad -\ 6 \qquad\ \ 3 + 2 = 6$$
$$\qquad\quad 0$$

ANSWER
$$\begin{array}{r} 463 \\ 2\overline{)926} \end{array}$$

Copy these problems to the Long Division – Hundreds printout and solve.

1.

Hundreds	Tens	Ones	
1	?	?	

$$5\overline{)6\ 7\ 5}$$
$$-\ ?\ ?\ ? \qquad 100 \times 5 = 500$$
$$\quad\ 1\ 7\ 5$$
$$-\ 1\ 5\ 0 \qquad\ 30 \times 5 = 150$$
$$\qquad\ ?\ ?$$
$$\qquad\ ?\ ? \qquad\quad 5 \times 5 = 25$$
$$\qquad\quad 0$$

2. $4\overline{)908}$

3. $2\overline{)726}$

4. $6\overline{)8,844}$

Worked Examples

You can use a shortcut method to solve division problems. In this Worked Example, you will see the base-10 blocks shown, so that you can understand how the shortcut method actually works. This is the "behind the scenes" work. But, when you work the problems using the shortcut method, you can just picture the blocks in your head, if that helps you. All you need to do is write the problem worked out as shown in Step 3 of the solution. The small number in the dividend shows the mental regrouping.

PROBLEM $2\overline{)726}$

SOLUTION

① Use the base-10 blocks to show 726 built with the fewest number of blocks possible.

② Write the problem.

③ Divide the 7 hundreds by 2. There will be 3 hundreds in each group and 1 hundred left over. Write a 3 in the hundreds place of the quotient. Break up the remaining hundred into 10 tens. Record them in the tens place of the dividend. You now have 12 tens altogether. You write a little 1 up by the 2 in the dividend to show that you now have 12 tens.

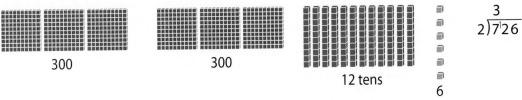

300   300   12 tens   6 ones

$$\begin{array}{r} 3 \\ 2\overline{)7^{1}26} \end{array}$$

④ Divide the 12 tens by 2. There will be 2 groups with 6 tens in each group. Write a 6 in the tens place of the quotient. There are no tens rods left over. There are only the 6 ones to divide by 2.

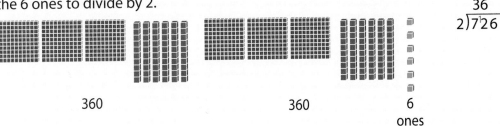

360   360   6 ones

$$\begin{array}{r} 36 \\ 2\overline{)7^{1}26} \end{array}$$

LEARN

5 Divide the 6 ones to make two groups with 3 in each group. Write a 3 in the ones place of the quotient.

363   363

$$\frac{363}{2\overline{)7\,26}}$$

ANSWER
$$\frac{363}{2\overline{)726}}$$

LOOK BACK You can use the inverse operation, multiplication, to check the answer to the division problem.

$$\begin{array}{r} {}^{1}\,363 \\ \times\ \ 2 \\ \hline 726 \end{array}$$

Solve using the shortcut method.

5. $2\overline{)722}$

6. $3\overline{)372}$

7. $5\overline{)805}$

8. $4\overline{)628}$

Divide Greater Numbers

Record Division Practice

Divide.

1. $7\overline{)854}$

2. $4\overline{)972}$

Choose the answer.

3. $238 \div 7 = ?$

    A. 54   B. 48   C. 43   D. 34

4. $495 \div 5 = ?$

    A. 109   B. 99   C. 90   D. 89

Divide.

5. $8\overline{)1,640}$

6. $3\overline{)1,350}$

7. $8\overline{)2,752}$

TRY IT

Different Ways to Divide (A)

Find Quotients

Use repeated subtraction to find the quotient.

1. $964 \div 4 = \underline{\ ?\ }$

2. $5{,}490 \div 6 = \underline{\ ?\ }$

Subtract to find the quotient.

3. $8\overline{)4{,}528}$

4. $3\overline{)279}$

Divide. Record the quotient above the division bracket.

5. $5\overline{)4{,}145}$

6. $7\overline{)238}$

Solve.

7. Charlie has 756 books arranged in 6 different bookcases. If each bookcase has the same number of books, how many books are in each one?

8. A sports shop has 1,944 baseball caps in stock. They are stored in boxes with 8 caps in a box. How many boxes of baseball caps does the store have?

9. Which division problem is incorrect? Explain the mistake in the problem.

A.
$$
\begin{array}{r}
356 \\
4\overline{)1{,}024} \\
-1{,}200 \\
\hline
224 \\
-200 \\
\hline
24 \\
-24 \\
\hline
0
\end{array}
$$

B.
$$
\begin{array}{r}
256 \\
4\overline{)1{,}024} \\
-800 \\
\hline
224 \\
-200 \\
\hline
24 \\
-24 \\
\hline
0
\end{array}
$$

TRY IT

10. Divide: $6\overline{)420}$. Choose the answer.

    A. 7   B. 70

    C. 80   D. 700

11. What is the quotient of 4,564 divided by 7? Choose the answer.

    A. 652   B. 642

    C. 256   D. $65\frac{2}{7}$

12. Divide 375 by 5.

13. Divide: $3\overline{)2,562}$.

14. Divide 6,265 by 7. Explain how to solve the problem.

15. Divide 390 by 6. Explain how to solve the problem.

16. Rachelle solved this division problem.
Explain the mistake Rachelle made and give the correct answer.

$$
\begin{array}{r}
54 \\
8\overline{)360} \\
-320 \\
\hline
40 \\
-40 \\
\hline
0
\end{array}
$$

17. Which number sentence solves the problem? Choose the answer.
Tom feeds his rabbits sunflower seeds. He uses 450 ounces in 6 months.
How many ounces of seeds does Tom use each month?

    A. $450 \div 6 = 57$ B. $450 \div 6 = 75$

    C. $450 \times 6 = 2,400$ D. $450 \times 6 = 2,700$

18. Jessie has 152 pencils. She wants to put them into packages of 8 pencils each.
How many packages of 8 pencils can Jessie make? Explain how to solve the problem.

TRY IT

Different Ways to Divide (B)

Remainders in Division

Worked Examples

You can show a remainder in a division problem two ways. How a remainder affects the final answer to a story problem depends on what the problem asks for.

PROBLEM   Divide: $139 \div 6 = ?$

SOLUTION 1   Estimate how many times 6 divides 139.

```
   23 r 1
6)139
 − 120
    19
 −  18
     1
```

Since 20 times 6 is 120, 6 divides 139 about 20 times (or 2 tens). Place the 2 above the tens place of the dividend.

Multiply 20 by 6. $20 \times 6 = 120$

Subtract $139 - 120$ to get 19. Divide 19 by 6. Write 3 above the ones place of the dividend.

Multiply 3 by 6. $3 \times 6 = 18$

$19 - 18 = 1$; 1 is less than the divisor 6, so 1 is the remainder.

SOLUTION 2   Make or draw a model.

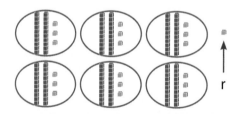

ANSWER   23 r 1

Divide. If there is a remainder, express the quotient with a remainder.

1. 6)457

2. 8)983

3. 9)345

4. 4)996

Worked Examples

PROBLEM 1 Marty is packing 141 books in boxes. Each box holds 6 books. How many boxes does Marty need to pack all the books?

SOLUTION

1 $141 \div 6 = 23 \text{ r } 3$

2 Marty has 3 books left over after he packs 23 boxes. Marty needs 1 more box for the 3 books.

3 So Marty needs 24 boxes to pack all the books.

ANSWER Marty needs 24 boxes.

PROBLEM 2 A clerk is arranging 141 toys on shelves at the toy store. If he puts 6 toys on a shelf, the shelf is full. How many shelves can the clerk fill?

SOLUTION

1 $141 \div 6 = 23 \text{ r } 3$

2 The 3 toys that are left over will not fill a shelf.

3 So the clerk can fill only 23 shelves.

ANSWER The clerk can fill 23 shelves.

PROBLEM 3 An athlete collected 141 medals in her lifetime. She wants to display them in glass cases in groups of 6. How many glass cases will she need to display all of her medals?

SOLUTION

1 $141 \div 6 = 23 \text{ r } 3$

2 There are 3 medals left over.

3 So she needs another glass case to display all of the medals.

ANSWER The athlete needs 24 glass cases.

L E A R N

Use the worked division problem shown here to answer Problems 5–7.

$$
\begin{array}{r}
336\ \text{r}\ 3 \\
4\overline{)1{,}347} \\
-\ 1{,}200 \\
\hline
147 \\
-\ 120 \\
\hline
27 \\
-\ 24 \\
\hline
3
\end{array}
$$

5. John has to read a 1,347-page book. He wants to finish the book in 4 weeks.
    How many pages will he have to read each week to complete the book?

    $1{,}347 \div 4 = \square$

6. There are 1,347 people waiting for a roller coaster. Each roller-coaster car
    holds 4 riders. How many cars will it take for all the people to have a ride?

    $1{,}347 \div 4 = \square$

7. Kelly and her friends are beading bags to sell at a craft show.
    They must sew 4 beads on each bag. They have 1,347 beads.
    How many bags can they bead?

    $1{,}347 \div 4 = \square$

Solve. Explain how you got your answer.

8. There are 277 players in a basketball league. There can be no more than
    9 players on each team. How many teams are needed in the league?

9. A machine at a factory cuts ribbon into pieces that are 4 inches long.
    A worker puts 4,550 inches of ribbon in the machine. How many
    4-inch pieces of ribbon will the machine cut?

LEARN

Different Ways to Divide (B)

Check Division

Worked Examples

You can check division by multiplying the quotient by the divisor and adding the remainder, if there is one.

PROBLEM Divide 316 by 6. Show how you checked your answer.

SOLUTION Estimate how many times 6 divides 316.

Since 50 times 6 is 300, 6 divides 316 about 50 times (or 5 tens). ⟶
Place the 5 above the tens place of the dividend.

Multiply 50 by 6. $50 \times 6 = 300$ ⟶

Subtract $316 - 300$ to get 16. Divide 16 by 6. ⟶
Write 2 above the ones place of the dividend.

Multiply 2 by 6. $2 \times 6 = 12$ ⟶

$16 - 12 = 4$; 4 is less than the divisor 6, so 4 is the remainder.

$$
\begin{array}{r}
52 \text{ r } 4 \\
6\overline{)316} \\
-300 \\
\hline
16 \\
-12 \\
\hline
4
\end{array}
$$

LOOK BACK Multiply the quotient by the divisor. Then add the remainder. If the result equals the dividend, the quotient is correct.

$$
\begin{array}{r}
52 \quad \leftarrow \text{quotient} \\
\times \ 6 \quad \leftarrow \text{divisor} \\
\hline
312 \\
+ \ 4 \quad \leftarrow \text{remainder} \\
\hline
316 \quad \leftarrow \text{dividend?}
\end{array}
$$

Write a number sentence to check each quotient. If the quotient shown is correct, write "correct." If the quotient shown is not correct, write "not correct."

1.
$$
\begin{array}{r}
289 \\
5\overline{)1,445}
\end{array}
$$

2.
$$
\begin{array}{r}
82 \text{ r } 3 \\
7\overline{)569}
\end{array}
$$

3.
$$
\begin{array}{r}
742 \text{ r } 1 \\
3\overline{)2,227}
\end{array}
$$

LEARN

Divide. If there is a remainder, express the quotient with a remainder and then as a mixed number. Then write a number sentence to check your answer.

4. $8\overline{)448}^{\,?}$

5. $2\overline{)137}^{\,?}$

6. $6\overline{)599}^{\,?}$

7. $4\overline{)1{,}732}^{\,?}$

8. $7\overline{)3{,}589}^{\,?}$

LEARN

Different Ways to Divide (B)

Divide and Check

Divide. If there is a remainder, express the quotient with a remainder.

1. $6\overline{)3,569}$

2. $9\overline{)1,806}$

Multiply to check each quotient. If the quotient shown is correct, write *correct*. If the quotient shown is not correct, write *not correct*.

3. $6\overline{)4,762}$ with quotient $794\ r\ 4$

4. $3\overline{)249}$ with quotient 83

Divide.

5. $4\overline{)132}$

6. $8\overline{)5,889}$

Choose the answer.

7. $5\overline{)544}$

   A. 18 r 4   B. 108   C. 108 r 4   D. 1084

Solve. Explain how you got your answer.

8. Campers are all going on canoe rides. One canoe can hold 6 people. There are 207 campers. How many canoes do they need?

9. Divide 2,623 by 9.

10. Aimee solved this division question. Explain the mistake Aimee made and give the correct answer.

$$
\begin{array}{r}
1,312 \\
6\overline{)788} \\
-6 \\
\hline
18 \\
-18 \\
\hline
8 \\
-6 \\
\hline
2
\end{array}
$$

TRY IT

11. Gino is making appetizers. He needs 3 cherry tomatoes for each mini pizza he is making. He has 178 tomatoes. How many pizzas can he make?

12. Joshua has 548 photographs. His album holds 8 photographs on each page. How many pages will he need to hold all his photographs?

Read the problem and follow the directions.

13. Helene solved this division problem. Show how Helene could check her work using multiplication. Is Helene correct?

$$\begin{array}{r} 874 \\ 6\overline{)2{,}868} \end{array}$$

14. Caroline was asked to put a number in the box to make this equation correct.

$$8\,\square\,1 \div 9 = 89$$

Caroline doesn't want to use the guess-and-check strategy. Explain a strategy that Caroline could use. Write the correct answer.

15. Nina solved this multiplication problem. Choose the expression she could use to check her work.

$$\begin{array}{r} 56 \\ \times\,12 \\ \hline 672 \end{array}$$

A. 12×672

B. 56×672

C. $672 \div 12$

D. $56 \div 12$

TRY IT

Prime Factors

Find Prime Factors

Make a factor tree for the composite number. Then show the composite number as the product of prime factors.

1. 42

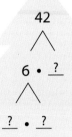

2. 20

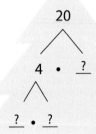

3. 27

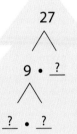

4. 48

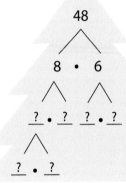

Read the problem and follow the directions.

5. Write the prime factors for 24.

6. Write the prime factors for 18.

7. Write 3 whole numbers less than 50 that have prime factors of only 2 or 3.

T R Y I T

Read the problem and follow the directions.

8. Allen said the prime factors for 45 are 5 • 9. Is he correct?
    If he is wrong, explain why he is wrong and write the correct answer.

9. Tom made this factor tree for 90. Make a different factor tree for 90.
    Write the prime factors for both trees.

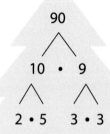

90

90

Choose the answer.

10. Which of the following shows the
    prime factors for 30?

    A. 2 • 3 • 5

    B. 5 • 6

    C. 1 • 2 • 2 • 5

    D. 3 • 10

11. Which of the following shows the
    prime factors for 28?

    A. 2 • 14

    B. 2 • 2 • 7

    C. 1 • 2 • 2 • 7

    D. 4 • 7

TRY IT

Solve.

1. Make two different factor trees for the composite number 36.

2. Show the prime factors for the composite number 36.

3. Gordon says the prime factors of 50 are 2 and 25. Is Gordon correct? If he is incorrect, explain why and write the correct answer.

4. Write the prime factors for 54. Explain how you know the factors are prime factors.

    (a) What were the prime factors?

    (b) Explain how you know the factors are prime factors.

5. Write three whole composite numbers between 10 and 50 that have prime factors of only 2 or 3.

TRY IT

5. State the actions and thinking you used during this lesson as a math learner.

Math Thinking and Actions
I made sense of problems by • Explaining to myself what a problem means and what it asks for • Using drawings or diagrams to represent a problem I was solving
I explained my math thinking clearly.
I tried out new ways to check if an answer is reasonable.
Other

TRY IT

Order of Operations (A)

Parentheses and Expressions

Worked Examples

Perform the operation or operations inside parentheses before all other operations. Changing the position of parentheses may change the value of the expression.

PROBLEM 1 $7 + 3 \times 6 + 2 = \underline{?}$

SOLUTION

$7 + \mathbf{3} \times \mathbf{6} + 2 = ?$ ⟵ Multiply.
$\mathbf{7 + 18} + 2 = ?$ ⟵ Add.
$\mathbf{25} + 2 = 27$ ⟵ Add.

ANSWER 27

PROBLEM 2 $(7 + 3) \times 6 + 2 = \underline{?}$

SOLUTION

$\mathbf{(7 + 3)} \times 6 + 2 = ?$ ⟵ Add inside parentheses.
$\mathbf{10 \times 6} + 2 = ?$ ⟵ Multiply.
$\mathbf{60 + 2} = 62$ ⟵ Add.

ANSWER 62

PROBLEM 3 $7 + 3 \times (6 + 2) = \underline{?}$

SOLUTION

$7 + 3 \times \mathbf{(6 + 2)} = ?$ ⟵ Add inside parentheses.
$7 + \mathbf{3 \times 8} = ?$ ⟵ Multiply.
$\mathbf{7 + 24} = 31$ ⟵ Add.

ANSWER 31

PROBLEM 4 $(7 + 3) \times (6 + 2) = \underline{?}$

SOLUTION

$\mathbf{(7 + 3)} \times (6 + 2) = ?$ ⟵ Add inside parentheses.
$10 \times \mathbf{(6 + 2)} = ?$ ⟵ Add inside parentheses.
$\mathbf{10 \times 8} = 80$ ⟵ Multiply.

ANSWER 80

Copy the following expression into your Math Notebook three times—at the top, middle, and bottom of a blank page. Leave a few blank lines beneath each expression.

$$2 + 3 \times 4 - 1 = ?$$

1. In the top expression, put parentheses around (3×4) and evaluate.

2. In the middle expression, put parentheses around $(4 - 1)$ and evaluate.

3. In the bottom expression, put parentheses around $(2 + 3)$ and evaluate.

L E A R N

Place one set of parentheses in the expression to make it true.

   4. $24 + 8 \div 4 - 2 = 6$

   5. $24 + 8 \div 4 - 2 = 28$

   6. $6 \times 15 \div 3 + 2 = 32$

   7. $6 \times 15 \div 3 + 2 = 18$

Evaluate the expression.

   8. $(2 + 3) \times (4 - 1) = \underline{\ \ ?\ \ }$

   9. $(4 + 20) \div (3 - 1) = \underline{\ \ ?\ \ }$

   10. $(5 + 12) \times (18 \div 9) = \underline{\ \ ?\ \ }$

   11. $(10 - 7) + (8 - 3) = \underline{\ \ ?\ \ }$

Write the number that makes the number sentence true.

   12. $5 \times (\underline{\ \ ?\ \ } - 2) = 35$

   13. $(10 \times 2) \div \underline{\ \ ?\ \ } = 2$

   14. $\underline{\ \ ?\ \ } \times (3 + 5) = 32$

Write $+$, $-$, $\times$, or $\div$ to make the number sentence true.

   15. $(3 \times 5) \underline{\ \ ?\ \ } 10 \div 2 = 10$

   16. $2 + (5 \underline{\ \ ?\ \ } 3) - 1 = 16$

   17. $4 + 7 - 3 \div 1 \underline{\ \ ?\ \ } 2 = 6$

LEARN

Order of Operations (A)

Evaluating Expressions

Memory Jogger

ORDER OF OPERATIONS

- First compute inside all parentheses.
- Next perform multiplication and division as the symbols appear from left to right.
- Then perform addition and subtraction as the symbols appear from left to right.

Solve. Explain your steps.

1. $10 \div 2 + (5 + 6) = \underline{\ ?\ }$

2. $16 \div 4 \times 2 = \underline{\ ?\ }$

3. $8 - 5 + 14 \div 2 = \underline{\ ?\ }$

4. $(3 + 4) \times (12 - 5) = \underline{\ ?\ }$

5. $4 + 20 \div 2 \times 3 = \underline{\ ?\ }$

6. $20 - (15 - 3) \div 2 = \underline{\ ?\ }$

Write the number that makes the number sentence true.

7. $7 + \square \times 2 = 17$

8. $2 \times (3 + \square) \div 4 = 6$

Write the operation symbol $(+, -, \times, \div)$ that makes the number sentence true.

9. $15 \ \square \ 3 + 5 = 10$

10. $15 - (6 \ \square \ 2) + 11 = 18$

T R Y   I T

Place parentheses in the expression to make the number sentence true.

11. $7 + 5 \div 3 + 12 = 16$ **12.** $27 \div 9 \div 3 - 5 = 4$ **13.** $20 = 6 + 4 \times 2$

Choose the answer.

14. $2 - (2 \times 1)$

   A. 0   B. 1   C. 2   D. 3

Read the problem and follow the directions.

15. Miraiah got the same answer when she solved $28 - 14 \div 2$ and $(28 - 14) \div 2$. Is she correct? Explain why or why not.

16. Dallas got the same value for these two expressions. Is he correct? Explain why or why not.

- $8 \times (3 + 9)$
- $8 \times 3 + 9$

17. Derrick got the same value for these two expressions. Is he correct? Explain why or why not.

- $6 \times (3 - 3) + 1$
- $6 \times 3 - 3 + 1$

18. Frank got the same value for these two expressions. Is he correct? Explain why or why not.

- $(4 \times 6) + 4$
- $4 \times (6 + 4)$

19. Megan got the same value for these two expressions. Is she correct? Explain why or why not.

- $(9 \times 3) + (6 - 5)$
- $9 \times (3 + 6) - 5$

20. Richard and Cheryl solved these two equations.

- $8 \times 3 + 12 \div 4 = \underline{\ ?\ }$
- $8 \times (3 + 12) \div 4 = \underline{\ ?\ }$

Richard said the answer to both questions was 9. Cheryl said the answer to the first question was 27 and the answer to the second question was 30. Which student is correct? Explain the mistake that one of the students made.

21. Write an expression that is equal to 14 using only the numbers 2, 3, and 4.

TRY IT

The Distributive Property (A)

Evaluate Expressions

Write the missing number.

1. $2 \times (4 + 5) = 2 \times 4 + 2 \times \square$

2. $7 \times 5 - 7 \times 2 = 7 \times (\square - 2)$

3. $8 \times (9 - 3) = \square - 24$

4. $30 - 24 = \square \times (5 - 4)$

Use the distributive property or the order of operations to find the value of the expression in a different way.

5. $3 \times (6 - 3) = 3 \times 3 = 9$

6. $5 \times (3 - 1) = 15 - 5 = 10$

Use the order of operations to find the value of the expression in a different way.

7. $8 \times (4 + 6) = 32 + 48 = 80$

8. $7 \times (8 + 4) = 7 \times 12 = 84$

Use the distributive property to multiply.

9. $56 \times 8 = (50 + 6) \times 8 = 50 \times 8 + 6 \times 8 = \square + \square = \square$

10. $7 \times 29 = 7 \times (30 - 1) = \underline{\ ?\ }$

11. $35 \times 6 = \underline{\ ?\ }$

Choose the answer.

12. Carla solved $6 \times (5 + 9)$ by saying the next step is 6×14. Which shows a different way to solve $6 \times (5 + 9)$?

    A. $5 + 9 \times 6$

    B. $6 \times 5 + 9$

    C. $6 \times 5 + 6 \times 9$

13. Which number replaces the box to make this a true sentence?
    $8 \times (2 + 5) = 16 + \square$

    A. 7

    B. 13

    C. 40

    D. 56

T R Y   I T

Write **two** number sentences that could be used to solve the problem.

14. Ellen is making 13 prize packages for her team mates. She is putting 6 bouncy balls and 3 barrettes into each package. What is the total number of objects she will put into the 13 packages?

15. Ken has 12 friends over. He gives each friend 5 stickers and 4 pencils when they leave. What is the total number of objects Ken gave to his 12 friends?

16. Coach Scott has 19 players on his team. He made each player a welcome bag. He put 5 baseballs and 2 batting gloves in each welcome bag. What is the total number of objects he put in the 19 welcome bags?

Choose the **two** number sentences that could be used to solve the problem.

17. Ron has 14 friends at his party. He will give each friend 4 cars and 5 bouncy balls when they go home. What is the total number of toys he will give away?

    A. $14 \times (4 + 5) = \square$

    B. $14 \times 4 \times 5 = \square$

    C. $(14 \times 4) + (14 \times 5) = \square$

    D. $14 \times (4 \times 5) = \square$

18. Tim has a bucket for each of his 25 friends. Tim is going to put 12 shells in each bucket. How many shells does he need altogether?

    A. $25 + 12 = \square$

    B. $25 \times 12 = \square$

    C. $25 \times 10 + 25 \times 2 = \square$

    D. $25 \times 1 + 25 \times 2 = \square$

TRY IT

Story Problems: Solve and Check (A)

Choosing the Operation

Worked Examples

To solve a story problem, you must first understand what the problem asks you to find. Then you have to decide which operation to use to find the answer. After you compute, you must look back to make sure your answer makes sense.

PROBLEM Identify the operation you would use to solve the problem. Then solve.

- Mr. Nichols works at the roller-skating rink. He is replacing the wheels on the rental skates. He has 234 wheels. He puts 4 new wheels on each skate. How many skates will have all new wheels?

SOLUTION Division. Use the method that is easiest for you. One way is shown.

1 Separate 234 wheels into equal groups of 4. Division is the best operation to use.

2 $234 \div 4 = 58$ r 2, or 58 skates with 2 wheels left over

3 Read the problem again to decide which to do:

- Drop the remainder.
- Increase the quotient by 1.
- Express the remainder as a fraction.

4 Remember that the problem asks how many skates will have all new wheels. A skate must have 4 wheels, so 2 wheels are not enough for another skate. Drop the remainder. 58 skates will have all new wheels.

ANSWER division; 58

L E A R N

Identify the operation you would use to solve the problem. Then solve.

1. Cody and Tyler launched model rockets. Tyler's rocket soared 1,418 feet. Cody's rocket reached a height 162 feet less than Tyler's rocket. How high, in feet, did did Cody's rocket fly?

2. In 2006, there were 1,135 people at a music festival. In 2008, 1,700 more people attended than in 2006. How many people attended the music festival in 2008?

3. The veterans collected coats for their annual coat drive. Donated coats have come from 1,652 people in the community. Each person gave 4 coats. How many coats did the veterans collect in all?

4. The art council collected $56,218 in donations. The council used $32,187 to fund an art camp. How much money does the art council have left?

5. Sven works at the movie theater. He earns $8 an hour. He is saving money to buy a new bike. The bike costs $312. How many hours does Sven need to work to be able to buy the bike?

6. Cindy wore a pedometer to record the number of steps she walked in a day. She walked 9,784 steps. Each of her steps measures 2 feet long. How many total feet did Cindy walk in a day?

7. There were 287 customers at the photo shop in the morning. In the afternoon, 53 different customers entered the shop. How many total customers came to the photo shop that day?

Story Problems: Solve and Check (A)

Story Problems

Identify the operation you would use to solve the problem. Then solve.

1. An empty plane weighs 176,650 pounds. The cargo and passengers weigh 117,280 pounds. What is the weight of the plane at takeoff?

2. An airplane can hold 255 passengers. On a flight from New York to Chicago, 32 seats are empty. How many passengers are on the plane?

3. Sam is building a model train display. He spends 4 hours each day working on it. He completes the display after 96 days. How many total hours did Sam spend building the display?

4. The bakery received an order for 182 blueberry muffins. The baker made the muffins and placed the muffins in boxes. Each box holds 6 muffins. How many boxes did the baker need to hold all the muffins?

Answer the question.

5. Small rosebushes cost $9 each. How many small rosebushes can Penny buy for $135?

6. A giraffe spends 20 hours a day grazing for food. How many hours would it spend grazing in 45 days?

7. Look back at Problem 4. How did the remainder affect your answer? Explain.

8. Fernando knows $6 \times 4 = 24$. How will this help him solve the problem $24 \div 6$?

9. The farmer planted some seeds with a machine. He planted 32 rows of seeds. Each row had 3,987 seeds. How many seeds did he plant?

Choose the answer.

10. The kitchen supply company made 2,987 bags of toothpicks. Each bag had 98 toothpicks. How many toothpicks did the company make altogether?

   A. 298,700   B. 292,726   C. 221,626   D. 197,476

11. Sharon solved this division problem. Which expression could be used to check her work?

   A. $(698 \times 2) + 4$ B. $(698 \times 4) + 2$

   C. $(698 + 2) \times 4$ D. $(698 + 4) \times 2$

$$698\frac{2}{4}$$
$$4\overline{)2,794}$$

TRY IT

Story Problems: Solve and Check (B)

Check the Answer

Worked Examples

You can use the inverse operation to check a computation problem. Addition and subtraction are inverse operations. Multiplication and division are inverse operations.

PROBLEM Identify the operation you would use to check the answer. Then use that operation to decide if the answer is correct. Write "Yes" if the answer is correct and "No" if the answer is not correct.

$$679 \div 6 = 113 \, r \, 1$$

SOLUTION

1 Since the problem is a division problem, its inverse operation is multiplication. To check it, you multiply and then add the remainder.

2 $113 \times 6 = 678$ and $678 + 1 = 679$

3
$$
\begin{array}{r}
113 \\
\times \quad 6 \\
\hline
678 \\
+ \quad 1 \\
\hline
679
\end{array}
$$

4 Since $113 \times 6 + 1 = 679$, then the answer is correct.

ANSWER multiplication and then add the remainder; Yes

Write the operation you would use to check the answer. Then use that operation to decide if the answer is correct. Write "Yes" if the answer is correct and "No" if the answer is not correct.

1.
$$
\begin{array}{r}
5,682 \\
+ \quad 739 \\
\hline
6,421
\end{array}
$$

2.
$$
\begin{array}{r}
259 \\
\times \quad 8 \\
\hline
1,602
\end{array}
$$

3. $13,451 - 5,608 = 7,855$

4. $368 \div 5 = 73 \, r \, 3$

LEARN

Write the operation you would use to check the solution to the story problem. Then use that operation to decide if the solution is correct. Write "Yes" if the solution is correct and "No" if the solution is not correct.

5. Each year, the local town hosts a music and art festival. Last year, there were 935,000 people at the festival. This year 17,000 more people attended the festival. How many people attended the festival this year?
   Solution: 952,000

6. Sven works at the movie theater. He earns $8 an hour. He is saving money to buy a new bike. The bike costs $312. How many hours does Sven need to work to be able to buy the bike?
   Solution: 39 hours

7. Cindy bought a giant box of paper clips for the office. There are 9,784 paper clips in the box. Each of the paper clips weighs 2 grams. How many grams do the paper clips weigh in total?
   Solution: 19,488 grams

8. Mr. Nichols works at the roller-skating rink. He is replacing the wheels on the rental skates. He has 232 wheels. He puts 4 new wheels on each skate. How many skates will have all new wheels?
   Solution: 58

Solve and check.

9. There are 1,572 books on each of 6 shelves at the library. How many books are there in all?

10. There are 450,486 sheets of card stock on the shelf at the office supply store. There are 23,115 more sheets of white paper than card stock. How many sheets of white paper are on the shelf?

11. There are 176,050 people living in the city where Pam lives. There are 150,280 fewer people living in the city where Craig lives than where Pam lives. How many people are living in the city where Craig lives?

Story Problems: Solve and Check (B)

Is the Answer Correct?

Write the expression to use to check the answer.

1. $72 \times 8 = 576$
2. $3{,}613 - 154 = 3{,}459$
3. $753 \div 6 = 125 \text{ r } 3$

Read the problem and follow the directions.

4. The movie theater can seat a maximum of 562 people for each show. Eight shows had every seat filled. The manager thought a total of 4,486 people were at the movies. Is the manager correct? If not, write the correct answer.

5. City planners had lots of money in the bank. They took out $6,876 to pay for some trees. They had $942,783 left. How much money did they have in the beginning?

   Dave solved this problem and said the answer was $949,559. Is he correct? If not, write the correct answer.

6. The roof of an arena is made of tiles. There are 428,001 white tiles and 428,005 cream tiles. How many tiles are on the roof in all?

   Haley solved this problem and said the answer was 856,006. Is she correct? If not, write the correct answer.

7. The green turtle nests on Ascension Island. One year there were 14,765 turtle nests on the island. The next year there were 8,654 nests. How many fewer nests were there the second year?

   Julie solved this problem and said the answer was 6,111. Is she correct? If not, write the correct answer.

8. A music store has 16 drum sets. Each drum set has 4 cymbals. How many cymbals are there in all?

   Fred solved this problem and said the answer was 61. Is he correct? If not, write the correct answer.

9. A warehouse stored 3,624 cans of soup. The cans were divided equally on 8 shelves. How many cans of soup were on each shelf?

   Maria solved this problem and said the answer was 354. Is she correct? If not, write the correct answer.

TRY IT

Choose the answer.

10. Some fishermen caught 146,356 fish the first week and 218,406 fish the second week. How many more fish did they catch the second week than the first week? Colleen said the answer to this story problem is 72,150. Which equation could be used to check her answer?

   A. $72,150 + 146,356 = 218,406$
      Colleen is correct.

   B. $72,150 + 146,356 = 218,506$
      Colleen is not correct.

   C. $218,406 - 72,150 = 146,356$
      Colleen is correct.

   D. $72,150 - 146,356 = 74,206$
      Colleen is not correct.

11. A baker put 8 buns into each bag. He made 5,432 buns last month. How many bags did the baker use? Which equation will verify the correct answer to this story problem?

   A. $40,246 \div 8 = 5,432$
      He used 40,246 bags.

   B. $43,456 \div 8 = 5,432$
      He used 43,456 bags.

   C. $679 \times 8 = 5,432$
      He used 679 bags.

   D. $681 \times 8 = 5,432$
      He used 681 bags.

12. A humpback whale migrated 3,583 miles. It will travel another 1,517 miles to reach its feeding grounds. Richard said the whale will travel a total of 5,100 miles. Michael said the whale will travel a total of 4,090 miles. Which expression verifies the correct answer?

   A. $5,100 - 3,583$
      Richard is correct.

   B. $4,090 - 1,517$
      Michael is correct.

   C. $4,090 + 1,517$
      Michael is correct.

   D. $5,100 + 3,583$
      Richard is correct.

13. The airline owns 7 planes. Each plane can carry 343 passengers. What is the total number of passengers that can be on the planes at one time? Which equation can be used to check the answer to this story problem?

   A. $343 \div 7 = 49$
      There can be 49 passengers on the planes at one time.

   B. $343 \times 7 = 2,101$
      There can be 2,101 passengers on the planes at one time.

   C. $2,101 \div 7 = 343$
      There can be 2,101 passengers on the planes at one time.

   D. $2,401 \div 7 = 343$
      There can be 2,401 passengers on the planes at one time.

TRY IT

Solve Story Problems

Solve.

1. Carren wants to make some floral baskets. Six floral baskets will each have 14 red roses and 10 white roses. Two floral baskets will each have 12 pink carnations and 8 white carnations. Carren wants to know how many flowers she needs in all.

    (a) Write an equation to model the problem. Use a letter to represent the unknown amount.

    (b) How many flowers does Carren need in all? Explain how you know.

2. Don has 6 boxes that each have 25 comic books and 13 comic-pricing guides. He gives his friend 3 boxes that each have 15 comic books and 4 pricing guides. Don wants to know the number of comic books and pricing guides he has left.

    (a) Write an equation to model the problem. Use a letter to represent the unknown amount.

    (b) How many comic books and pricing guides does Don have left? Explain how you know.

    (c) Check if your answer is reasonable. Explain how you know. If your answer is not reasonable, correct errors and solve the problem.

3. Seven buses holding 103 people each traveled to the stadium. Three of the buses returned home early. Each bus that returned home early had 44 adults and 12 children. Figure out how many people were left to travel home on the remaining 4 buses.

    (a) Write an equation to model the problem. Use a variable to represent the unknown amount.

    (b) How many people were left to travel on the remaining buses? Explain how you know.

    (c) Check if your answer is reasonable. Explain how you know. If your answer is not reasonable, solve the problem again.

    (d) If each bus can hold a maximum of 120 people, will all of the people be able to travel home on the buses?

TRY IT

4. Love Our Animals has 7 shelters for cats and dogs. Each shelter houses 26 cats, 40 kittens, 18 dogs, and 22 puppies. Determine how many more kittens and puppies the organization has than cats and dogs.

   (a) Write an equation to model the problem. Use a variable to represent the unknown amount.

   (b) How many more kittens and puppies does the organization have than cats and dogs? Explain how you know.

   (c) How many total animals are at all 7 shelters? Explain how you know.

Think Like a Mathematician Self-Check

5. State the actions and thinking you used during this lesson as a math learner.

Math Thinking and Actions
I made sense of problems by   • Explaining to myself what a problem means and what it asks for   • Using drawings or diagrams to represent a problem I was solving
I explained my math thinking clearly.
I tried out new ways to check if an answer is reasonable.
Other

TRY IT

Line Pairs

Identify and Draw Lines and Line Segments

Identify pairs of lines or line segments as *intersecting*, *parallel*, or *perpendicular*.

1.

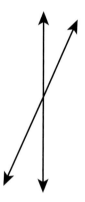

2.

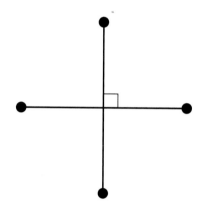

3.

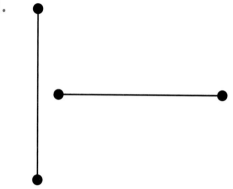

4.

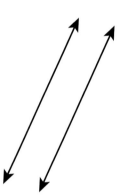

TRY IT

Choose the word or words that describe the pair of lines or line segments.

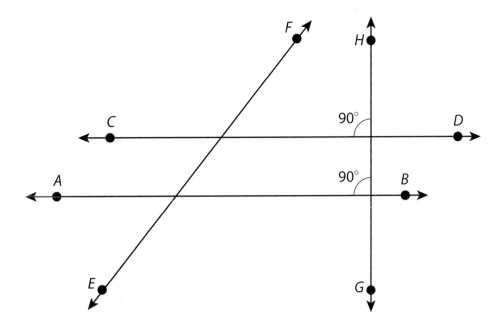

5. $\overleftrightarrow{AB}$ and $\overleftrightarrow{CD}$

    A. parallel

    B. intersecting

    C. perpendicular

6. $\overleftrightarrow{AB}$ and $\overleftrightarrow{EF}$

    A. parallel

    B. intersecting

    C. perpendicular

7. $\overleftrightarrow{AB}$ and $\overleftrightarrow{GH}$

    A. parallel

    B. intersecting

    C. perpendicular

8. $\overleftrightarrow{CD}$ and $\overleftrightarrow{EF}$

    A. parallel

    B. intersecting

    C. perpendicular

Draw the pair of lines or line segments.

9. a pair of perpendicular line segments that intersect

10. a pair of parallel line segments

11. a pair of parallel lines

12. a pair of perpendicular lines

13. a pair of perpendicular line segments that do not intersect

TRY IT

Types of Angles

Draw Rays and Angles

Rays are drawn as straight lines with a dot at one end indicating the endpoint and an arrow at the other end indicating that the ray has no endpoint in that direction. Pairs of rays form angles, with their shared endpoint forming the vertex. Rays and angles can be labeled using letters.

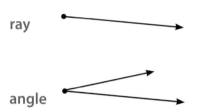

ray

angle

ray PQ

angle XYZ

Draw each figure using a ruler.

1. Draw a ray.

2. Draw and label ray *AB*.

3. Draw pairs of rays to form each angle.

   (a) acute angle

   (b) right angle

   (c) straight angle

   (d) obtuse angle

4. Draw and label ray *DC* and ray *DE* to form a straight angle *CDE*.

TRY IT

Angles and Rotation

Turns and Angles

Worked Examples

You can find how many turns or rotations through an angle it takes to make a full turn of a circle.

PROBLEM 1 How many turns through a 90° angle will create a complete circle, so that there are no gaps?

STEP 1   **STEP 2**   **STEP 3**

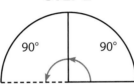

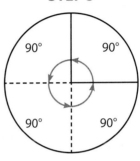

SOLUTION

1 Begin with a 90° angle drawn.

2 Rotate this angle 90° to the left to create another 90° angle.

3 Repeat two more times to make a complete turn of the circle. Notice that a total of four 90° angles create the circle.

ANSWER Four turns through a 90° angle create a complete circle with no gaps.

PROBLEM 2 How many turns through a 45° angle will create a complete turn of a circle?

STEP 1   **STEP 2**   **STEP 3**

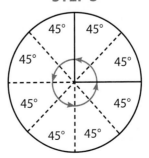

L E A R N

1 Begin with a 90° angle drawn. Remember that it takes turns through four 90° angles to create a full turn of a circle.

2 Make two 45° angles by separating the 90° angle into two equal parts.

3 Turn this pair of 45° angles until you have a circle. Eight 45° angles create a full circle. You can also multiply to find that there are eight 45° angles: Four 90° angles create a circle, and two 45° angles create a 90° angle, so $4 \times 2 = 8$, or eight 45° angles.

ANSWER Eight turns through a 45° angle create a complete circle with no gaps.

PROBLEM 3 How many turns through a 1° angle will create a full turn through a circle?

SOLUTION Since ninety 1° angles are in a 90° angle, and four 90° angles create a full turn of a circle, then $4 \times 90 = 360$. To create a circle, you need 360 turns through a 1° angle.

ANSWER Three hundred sixty turns through a 1° angle create a full turn through a circle.

Problem 3 leads to a definition for a degree:

A **degree** (with symbol °) is the angle measure that, when turned or rotated through 360 times, creates a circle.

PROBLEM 4 What is the degree measure for an angle that takes 10 turns through to create a circle?

SOLUTION

1 Write the problem as a multiplication statement: $10 \times \underline{\hspace{1cm}} = 360$.

2 Rewrite as a division statement: $360 \div 10 = \underline{\hspace{1cm}}$. So 10 turns through a 36° angle will create a circle.

ANSWER Ten turns through a 36° angle create a circle.

Determine the number of turns needed through the angle to make a full turn of a circle.

1. 180° angle

2. 60° angle

3. 18° angle

4. 9° angle

Determine the angle measure needed to create a full turn of a circle for the number of turns.

5. 5 turns

6. 12 turns

7. 36 turns

Angles and Rotation

Turns and Angle Measures

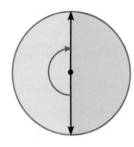

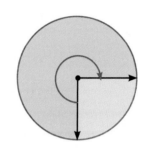

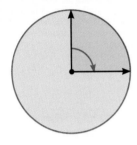

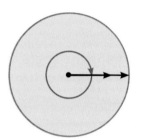

90°	180°	270°	360°
$\frac{1}{4}$ turn	$\frac{1}{2}$ turn	$\frac{3}{4}$ turn	full turn

Determine the angle measure. Then determine the fraction of the circle the angle rotates.

1.

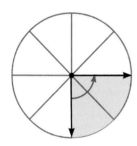

2.

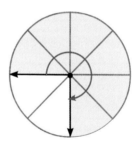

3.

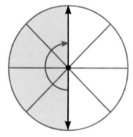

4.

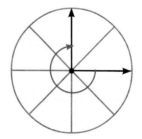

TRY IT

Choose the answer.

5.

What is the measure of the angle?

A. 90°

B. 135°

C. 180°

D. 270°

6.

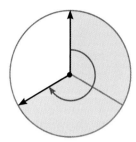

What is the measure of the angle?

A. 60°

B. 180°

C. 240°

D. 270°

7.

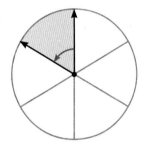

What is the measure of the angle?

A. 50°

B. 72°

C. 144°

D. 180°

8.

What is the measure of the angle?

A. 18°

B. 30°

C. 45°

D. 60°

Trace the circle. Sketch an angle with the given measure on the circle. Then determine the fraction of a turn the angle rotates.

9. 180°

10. 72°

11. 45°

12. 90°

13. 120°

14. 60°

TRY IT

Angles (A)

Measure Angles

Use a protractor to measure the angle. Write the angle measure.

1.

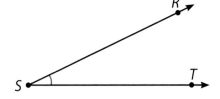

2.

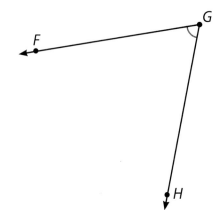

3.

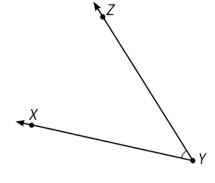

4.

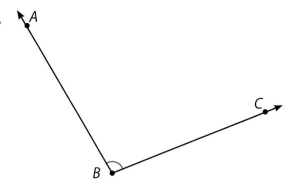

5.

TRY IT

6.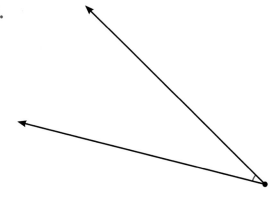

7.

Draw the given angle.

8. obtuse angle

9. acute angle

10. straight angle

11. 90° angle
Name the angle as either an acute angle, an obtuse angle, a right angle, or a straight angle.

Choose the answer.

12. Classify the angle.

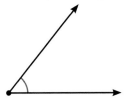

A. acute

B. obtuse

C. right

D. straight

13. Classify the angle.

A. acute

B. obtuse

C. right

D. straight

14. Which is an obtuse angle?

A.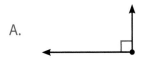

B.

C.

D.

TRY IT

Angles (B)

Draw and Measure Angles

Use a protractor to measure the angle. Record the measures and describe the angle as acute, right, obtuse, or straight.

1.

2.

3.
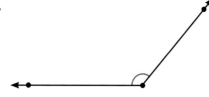

4.

Use a ruler and a protractor to draw the angle to the given measure. Describe the angle as acute, right, obtuse, or straight.

5. 110°

6. 35°

7. 90°

8. Draw a straight angle, label the center *B*, and show the angle measure.

9. Draw a 45° angle.

10. Draw a 120° angle.

11. Draw a 160° angle.

12. Draw a 180° angle.

TRY IT

Add and Subtract Angle Measures
Find Missing Angle Measures

Worked Examples

When an angle is decomposed into two nonoverlapping angles, the sum of the measures of the two parts is equal to the measure of the whole (the entire original angle). You can add or subtract to find a missing angle measure.

PROBLEM 1 Find the missing angle measure.

$m\angle 1 = 150°$

$m\angle 2 = ?$

$m\angle 3 = 84°$

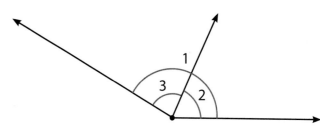

SOLUTION

1 Write an equation to relate the angle measures.

$m\angle 2 = m\angle 1 - m\angle 3$

2 Substitute the known angle measures and solve.

$m\angle 2 = 150° - 84°$

$m\angle 2 = 66°$

ANSWER $m\angle 2 = 66°$

PROBLEM 2 David is laying tiles. He lays a square tile and a triangular tile as shown. What is the measure of the angle formed by the two tiles?

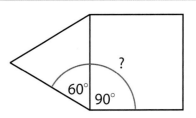

SOLUTION

1 Determine how the known and unknown angle measures relate.

The measure of the angle formed by the triangle plus the measure of the angle formed by the square equals the measure of the angle formed by the two tiles.

2 Substitute the known angle measures and solve.

$60° + 90° = m\angle 1$

$150° = m\angle 1$

ANSWER The measure of the angle formed by the two tiles is 150°.

LEARN

Find the missing angle measure.

1. $m\angle 1 = ?$
    $m\angle 2 = 75°$
    $m\angle 3 = 25°$

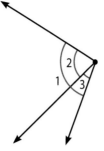

2. $m\angle 1 = ?$
    $m\angle 2 = 15°$
    $m\angle 3 = 67°$

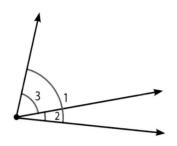

3. $m\angle 1 = 90°$
    $m\angle 2 = ?$
    $m\angle 3 = 52°$

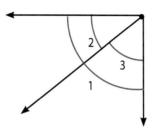

4. $m\angle 1 = 128°$
    $m\angle 2 = 54°$
    $m\angle 3 = ?$

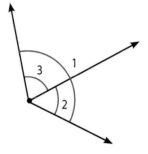

5. $m\angle 1 = ?$
    $m\angle 2 = 90°$
    $m\angle 3 = 90°$

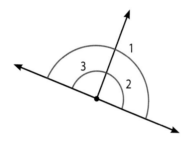

6. $m\angle 1 = 71°$
    $m\angle 2 = 42°$
    $m\angle 3 = ?$

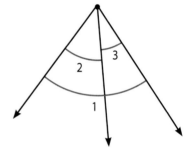

Answer the question.

7. Abby wants to see how the incline of a ramp affects how fast a toy car will roll down it. First she tries rolling a car down a ramp with a 37° incline. Then she tries a ramp with an incline of 62°. How many degrees steeper is the second ramp?

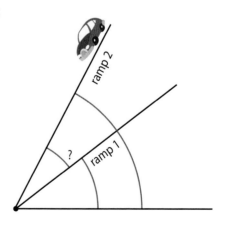

8. Ana looks up 35° to see the top of a tree. Then she looks up 13° higher to the top of the building behind the tree. From Ana's viewpoint, at what angle must she look up to see the top of the building?

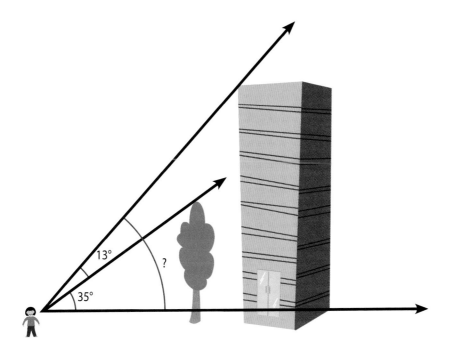

9. Erin and Brooke are sitting on the floor with their backs touching. Erin bends forward 43°. What angle does Brooke's body form?

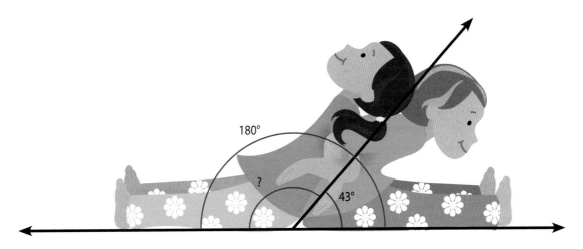

Solve.

1. $\angle 1 = 158°$
   $\angle 2 = 68°$
   $\angle 3 = ?$

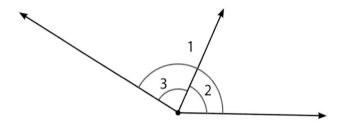

   (a) Write an equation that could be used to find $m \angle 3$. Use a letter to represent the unknown measure.

   (b) Solve the equation you wrote in Part (a). What is $m \angle 3$?

   (c) Ryan says that $\angle 3$ is an acute angle. Is Ryan correct? Explain why or why not.

2. Tanaya is building a bookshelf against the wall of her bedroom. She wants to find the measure of the angle of her book on the shelf, $m \angle 4$. If $m \angle 3 = 136°$, what is $m \angle 4$? Explain how you found your answer.

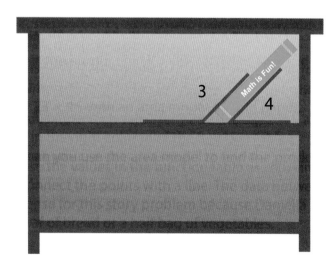

TRY IT

3. Decompose an obtuse angle into two nonoverlapping acute angles.

(a) Use a ruler and protractor to draw an obtuse angle. Label the vertex *A* and note the measure of the angle.

(b) On your angle from Part (a), use a ruler and protractor to draw a ray from vertex *A* that decomposes the angle into two acute angles. Note the measures of the two acute angles formed.

(c) Write two different equations that show how the measures of the obtuse angle and the two acute angles are related.

Think Like a Mathematician Self-Check

4. State the actions and thinking you used during this lesson as a math learner.

Math Thinking and Actions
I made sense of problems by • Explaining to myself what a problem means and what it asks for • Using drawings or diagrams to represent a problem I was solving
I explained my math thinking clearly.
I tried out new ways to check if an answer is reasonable.
Other

TRY IT

Fractions

Model Fractions

Write the fraction that the shaded part of the figure represents.

1.

2.

3.

4.

5.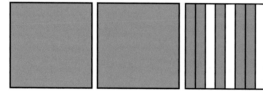

6.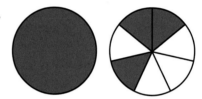

Answer the question.

7. Bobby wants to model $\frac{6}{11}$ by shading parts of the rectangle shown. How many parts should he shade? Explain.

8. Why is $\frac{5}{5}$ equal to 1 whole?

9. Why is $\frac{4}{4}$ the same as 1 whole?

Choose the answer.

10. Which shows $\frac{1}{4}$ shaded?

A.    B.   C.   D.

T R Y   I T

11. Which shows $\frac{8}{11}$ shaded?

A. 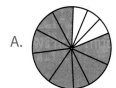   B. 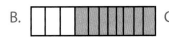 C.  D.

12. Which explains how to show $\frac{5}{5}$?

   A. Draw 10 circles, all the same size, and shade 5 of them.

   B. Draw 5 triangles and 5 squares, and shade the 5 triangles.

   C. Draw a rectangle divided into 5 equal parts, and shade 5 parts.

   D. Draw a circle divided into 10 equal parts, and shade 5 parts.

13. Which explains how to show $\frac{9}{9}$?

   A. Draw a square divided into 9 equal parts, and shade all 9 parts.

   B. Draw 9 squares all the same shape and size, and shade 1 square.

   C. Draw a circle with a 9 in the middle, and shade the circle.

   D. Draw 9 squares all the same shape and size, and shade 1 square.

14. Melissa saw $\frac{6}{6}$ of the cake. Which statement is true?

   A. Melissa saw 1 whole cake.

   B. Melissa saw less than 1 whole cake.

   C. Melissa saw more than 1 whole cake.

15. Which shows $\frac{2}{2}$ shaded?

A.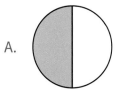

B.

C.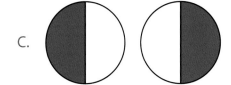

D.

TRY IT

Sketch Fractions

Draw Fractions

Worked Examples

You can represent a fraction as a part of a whole, as a part of a set, or as a location on the number line.

PROBLEM 1 Make three sketches to show $\frac{7}{12}$ as a part of a whole, as a part of a set, and as a location on a number line.

SOLUTION 1 $\frac{7}{12}$ as a part of a whole

The whole is divided into 12 equal sections. 7 of the sections are shaded.

SOLUTION 2 $\frac{7}{12}$ as a part of a set

There are 12 objects in the set. 7 of the objects are circles.

SOLUTION 3 $\frac{7}{12}$ as a location on the number line

Each tick mark represents one-twelfth.

The point is on the 7th twelfth.

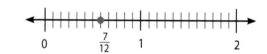

ANSWER

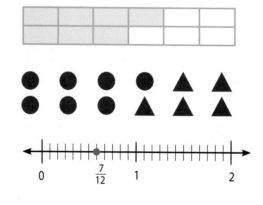

LEARN

Read the problem and follow the directions.

1. Make a sketch to represent $\frac{5}{6}$ as a part of a whole.

2. Make a sketch to represent $\frac{3}{7}$ as a part of a set.

3. Make a sketch to represent $\frac{4}{10}$ as a location on a number line.

4. Make a sketch to represent $\frac{10}{12}$.

5. Draw two rectangles that are the same size and shape.
   Divide one to show thirds. Divide one to show fifths.
   Which are larger, thirds or fifths? Use your drawings to explain.

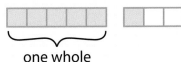

You can represent a mixed number more than one way.

PROBLEM 2 Sketch two rectangles and show that $\frac{6}{5}$ is the same as $1\frac{1}{5}$.

SOLUTION If $\frac{5}{5}$ equals 1 whole, then 6 fifths, or $\frac{6}{5}$, are shaded.
If $\frac{5}{5}$ equals 1 whole, then 1 whole and 1 fifth, or $1\frac{1}{5}$, are shaded.

ANSWER

one whole

PROBLEM 3 Sketch two number lines and show that $\frac{26}{9}$ is the same as $2\frac{8}{9}$.

SOLUTION The point is located at $\frac{26}{9}$ as well as $2\frac{8}{9}$, so $\frac{26}{9}$ and $2\frac{8}{9}$ both name the same location on the number line, and $\frac{26}{9} = 2\frac{8}{9}$.

ANSWER

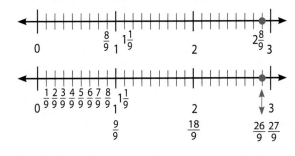

Read the problem and follow the directions.

6. Make a sketch that shows that $2\frac{2}{3} = \frac{8}{3}$.

L E A R N

Sketch Fractions

Fraction Sketches

Make a sketch to show the fraction.

1. $\frac{3}{4}$ as a part of a whole

2. $\frac{5}{7}$ as a part of a set

3. $\frac{1}{3}$ as a location on a number line

4. $3\frac{1}{4}$ as a part of a whole

5. $\frac{10}{12}$ as a part of a whole, as a part of a set, and as a location on a number line

Read the problem and follow the directions.

6. Put a dot on this number line to show the mixed number $3\frac{1}{4}$.

7. Shade $\frac{2}{6}$ of these objects.

8. Shade $\frac{1}{3}$ of these apples.

9. Shade $2\frac{4}{5}$ of these circles.

10. Draw 12 circles. Shade $\frac{5}{6}$ of them.

11. Shade $\frac{5}{7}$ of this rectangle.

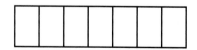

12. Put a dot on this number line to show the number $\frac{7}{12}$.

T R Y   I T

Different Meanings of Fractions (A)

Fraction Meanings

Story Problem	Model	Fraction
Maggie walked $\frac{2}{4}$ mile on a straight road, stopped for a rest, and then walked $\frac{1}{4}$ mile farther. What fraction of a mile did Maggie walk in all?	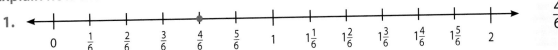 0 $\frac{1}{4}$ $\frac{2}{4}$ $\frac{3}{4}$ 1 $1\frac{1}{4}$ $1\frac{2}{4}$ $1\frac{3}{4}$ 2	$\frac{3}{4}$
Maggie has a container of 12 eggs. She cooks 8 eggs. What fraction of the eggs does Maggie cook?	○○○○○○○○○○○○	$\frac{8}{12}$
Maggie's house has 2 glass doors side-by-side. Each has 6 square panels. Maggie cleaned 6 of the panels in one door and 1 in the other door. What fraction of a door did Maggie clean?		$1\frac{1}{6}$

Explain how the model shows the fraction.

1.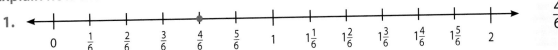
0   $\frac{1}{6}$ $\frac{2}{6}$ $\frac{3}{6}$ $\frac{4}{6}$ $\frac{5}{6}$ 1 $1\frac{1}{6}$ $1\frac{2}{6}$ $1\frac{3}{6}$ $1\frac{4}{6}$ $1\frac{5}{6}$ 2 $\frac{4}{6}$

2.  $\frac{7}{9}$

3.  $\frac{10}{13}$

TRY IT

Solve. Sketch the model.

4. Nick has a board that is 1 foot, 5 inches long. Since 1 foot equals 12 inches, what fraction or mixed number, written as twelfths, describes the length of Nick's board?

5. Leona made 8 cups of pudding. Her family ate 3 cups. What fraction of the cups of pudding were left?

6. Six cousins were together for a family reunion. Four of the cousins are girls. What fraction represents the number of boys?

Choose the answer.

7. This image shows $\frac{3}{4}$ shaded.
Which other image shows the same fraction?

A.

B.

C.

D.

8. This image shows $\frac{1}{3}$ shaded.
Which other image shows the same fraction?

A.

B.

C.

D.

9. This number line shows the fraction $\frac{2}{5}$.
Which other image shows the fraction $\frac{2}{5}$ shaded?

A.

B.

C.

D.

TRY IT

10. Which does **not** show $\frac{5}{6}$ shaded?

A.

B.

C.

D.

11. Which does **not** show $\frac{4}{9}$ shaded?

A.

B.

C.

D.

12. Which shows $\frac{3}{8}$ on a number line?

A.

B.

C.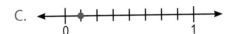

D.

13. Which shows $\frac{2}{5}$ on a number line?

A.

B.

C.

D.

TRY IT

14. Which shows $\frac{3}{4}$ on a number line?

A.

B.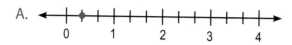

C.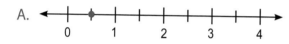

D.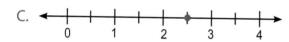

15. Which shows $2\frac{1}{3}$ on a number line?

A.

B.

C.

D.

16. Which shows $2\frac{1}{2}$ on a number line?

A.

B.

C.

D.

TRY IT

Different Meanings of Fractions (B)

Solve Fraction Problems

Solve.

1. A plumber needs to cut a 6-foot long pipe into 10 equal pieces. How long will each piece be?

2. Tony and Lisa equally share babysitting for a neighbor's child. If they babysit for 7 days in 1 week, how many days will each person babysit?

3. Karen bought 5 lemons and 7 oranges. What fraction of the fruit that she bought was oranges?

4. In New York City, there are 20 blocks in a mile. Tom walks 5 blocks from the train to his office every day. What part of a mile does he walk every day?

5. Emily bought 5 pounds of ground beef and divided it into 6 equal packages to freeze. How many pounds are in each package that Emily prepares?

6. Una cut a ribbon into 10 equal pieces. She sewed 7 pieces onto her quilt. What fraction of the ribbon did Una sew onto the quilt?

7. Sara lives 8 miles from her aunt's house. She rides her bike 6 miles and then stops to get a drink. What fraction of the trip to her aunt's house has Sara completed?

Choose the answer.

8. Which means the same as $\frac{3}{7}$?

   A. $\frac{1}{3} + \frac{1}{3} + \frac{1}{3} + \frac{1}{3} + \frac{1}{3} + \frac{1}{3} + \frac{1}{3}$

   B. $\frac{3}{3} + \frac{3}{3} + \frac{3}{3}$

   C. $\frac{1}{7} + \frac{1}{7} + \frac{1}{7}$

   D. $\frac{7}{7} + \frac{7}{7} + \frac{7}{7}$

9. Which means the same as $\frac{5}{4}$?

   A. $\frac{1}{5} + \frac{1}{5} + \frac{1}{5} + \frac{1}{5}$

   B. $\frac{5}{5} + \frac{5}{5} + \frac{5}{5} + \frac{5}{5}$

   C. $\frac{1}{4} + \frac{1}{4} + \frac{1}{4} + \frac{1}{4} + \frac{1}{4}$

   D. $\frac{4}{4} + \frac{4}{4} + \frac{4}{4} + \frac{4}{4} + \frac{4}{4}$

T R Y   I T

10. Which means the same as $2\frac{1}{4}$?

A. $\frac{1}{4}+\frac{1}{4}+\frac{1}{4}+\frac{1}{4}+\frac{1}{4}+\frac{1}{4}+\frac{1}{4}+\frac{1}{4}+\frac{1}{4}$

B. $\frac{1}{4}+\frac{1}{4}+\frac{1}{4}$

C. $\frac{1}{4}+\frac{1}{4}$

D. $\frac{2}{2}+\frac{2}{2}+\frac{2}{2}+\frac{2}{2}$

11. There are 10 balls in a bin, 7 yellow ones and 3 green ones. What fraction of the balls is yellow?

A. $\frac{7}{3}$ B. $\frac{7}{10}$ C. $\frac{3}{7}$ D. $\frac{10}{7}$

12. Emil cut a log into 8 equal pieces. He burned 3 pieces in his fireplace. Which number line shows the fraction of the log that was burned?

A.

B.

C.

D.

13. Suzanne cut a ribbon into 9 equal pieces. She sewed 5 pieces onto her quilt. Which number line shows the fraction of the ribbon that was sewn onto the quilt?

A.

B.

C.

D.

TRY IT

Different Meanings of Fractions (C)

Fractions as Ratios

Worked Examples

Fractions can show a *ratio*, or a comparison between two amounts. The order in which you are asked to compare amounts is important. The first amount in a ratio is the numerator. The second amount in a ratio is the denominator.

PROBLEM 1 Compare the length of the red segment to the length of the black segment. Then explain their relationship. Next express the ratio of the red to the black as a fraction.

SOLUTION

1 Trace the shorter segment. Cut it out.

2 Compare the length of the red segment to the black segment.

3 Count as you measure. ──────────→ 4 red segments = 1 black segment

4 Write a comparison sentence. ──────────→ The length of the red segment is $\frac{1}{4}$ of the length of the black segment.

5 Write the ratio of red to black as a fraction. ──────────→ The ratio of red to black is $\frac{1}{4}$.

ANSWER The length of the red segment is $\frac{1}{4}$ of the length of the black segment. The ratio of red to black is $\frac{1}{4}$.

L E A R N

PROBLEM 2 Compare the length of the red segment to the length of the black segment. Then explain their relationship. Next express the ratio of the red to the black as a fraction.

SOLUTION

1 Trace the shorter segment. Cut it out.

2 Compare the length of the red segment to the length of the black segment.

3 Count as you measure. ────────→ 1 red segment = 5 black segments

4 Write a comparison sentence. ────────→ The red segment is 5 times the length of the black segment.

5 Write the ratio of red to black as a fraction. ────────→ The ratio of red to black is $\frac{5}{1}$.

ANSWER The length of the red segment is 5 times the length of the black segment. The ratio of red to black is $\frac{5}{1}$.

Compare the length of the red segment to the length of the black segment. Then explain their relationship. Next express the ratio as a fraction.

1.

2.

3.

4.

5.

6.

7.

Different Meanings of Fractions (C)

Write Fractions to Compare

Solve.

1. The line segments show the lengths of a baby's shoe and an adult's shoe. What fraction can you use to compare the length of the baby's shoe to the length of the adult's shoe?

 baby's shoe

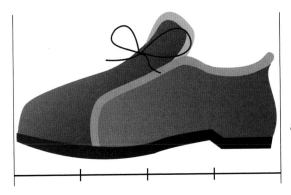 adult's shoe

2. What fraction can you write to compare line segment *A* to line segment *B*?

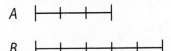

3. Caroline is 16 years old and Jim is 12 years old. What fraction compares Caroline's age to Jim's age?

4. What fraction can you write to compare line segment *A* to line segment *B*?

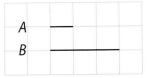

5. Sam's hand measures 5 inches and his arm measures 16 inches. Write a fraction to compare the length of Sam's hand to the length of his arm.

T R Y   I T

6. How many of line segment *C* does it take to measure line segment *D*?

   Write a fraction to compare the length of line segment *C* to line segment *D*.

   Write a fraction to compare the length of line segment *D* to line segment *C*.

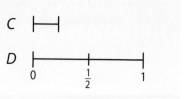

7. Hank had 3 pounds of hamburger meat and 4 pounds of hot dogs. What fraction tells the fraction of the pounds of hot dogs Hank had to the pounds of hamburger meat?

8. Marie had 12 pears in a bowl. She and her friends ate 5 pears. What fraction of the pears are left in the bowl?

9. Tanya is 2. Her brother is 5. What fraction represents Tanya's age compared to her brother's age?

10. Helen is 8. Her cousin is 12. What fraction represents Helen's age compared to her cousin's age?

Choose the answer.

11. Jacques cut a cucumber into 7 equal pieces. He ate 3 pieces. Which shows the fraction of the cucumber that was left?

   A.

   B.

   C.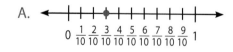

   D.

12. There were 10 ducks in the water. Three of the ducks got out of the water. Which shows the fraction of the ducks that are left in the water?

   A.

   B.

   C.

   D.

TRY IT

13. Dave had 9 library books. He returned 7 of them to the library. Which shows the fraction of the library books that he still has?

A.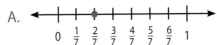

B.

C.

D.

14. Willa is 3. Her brother is 8. Which fraction represents Willa's age compared to her brother's age?

A. $\frac{3}{8}$

B. $\frac{5}{8}$

C. $\frac{3}{11}$

D. $\frac{8}{11}$

15. Saul has 2 bottles that he could use for his juice. One bottle holds 8 ounces. The other bottle holds 12 ounces. Which fraction represents how much the smaller bottle holds compared to the larger bottle?

A. $\frac{12}{8}$

B. $\frac{8}{20}$

C. $\frac{12}{20}$

D. $\frac{8}{12}$

16. Manny has a piece of ribbon that is 11 inches long. He wants to cut a piece that is 7 inches long for a decoration. Which fraction represents how long the piece for the decoration will be compared to the length of ribbon?

A. $\frac{6}{11}$

B. $\frac{7}{11}$

C. $\frac{11}{18}$

D. $\frac{7}{18}$

TRY IT

Explain Equivalent Fractions (A)

Show Equivalent Fractions

Explain how the pictures show that the fractions are equivalent.

1. $\frac{3}{4} = \frac{6}{8}$

$\frac{3}{4}$ $\frac{6}{8}$

2. $\frac{1}{2} = \frac{4}{8}$

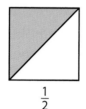

$\frac{1}{2}$ $\frac{4}{8}$

Complete the equation. Explain your answer.

3. $\frac{2}{5} = \frac{? \times 2}{? \times 5} = \frac{4}{10}$

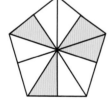

4. $\frac{1}{4} = \frac{? \times 1}{? \times 4} = \frac{4}{16}$

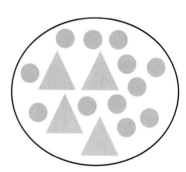

Tell whether the pair of fractions are equivalent.
Answer *Yes* or *No*, and explain your answer.

5. $\frac{2}{6}$ and $\frac{1}{3}$

6. $\frac{4}{10}$ and $\frac{2}{5}$

Sketch shapes or number lines to model the fractions. Then state whether or not the fractions or equivalent. Explain why or why not.

7. $\frac{2}{4}$ and $\frac{4}{8}$

8. $\frac{2}{4}$ and $\frac{1}{2}$

9. $\frac{5}{6}$ and $\frac{2}{3}$

10. $\frac{6}{10}$ and $\frac{3}{5}$

TRY IT

Explain Equivalent Fractions (B)

Equivalent or Not?

Use the number line to find four fractions that are equivalent to $\frac{1}{2}$.
Explain why the fractions are equivalent.

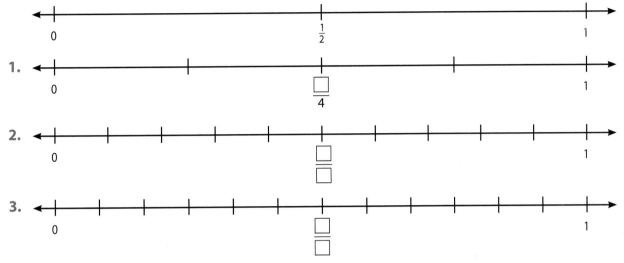

Use the number line to find three fractions that are equivalent to $\frac{1}{3}$. Explain why
the fractions are equivalent.

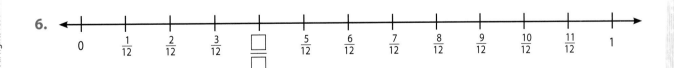

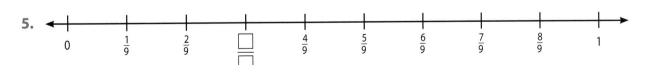

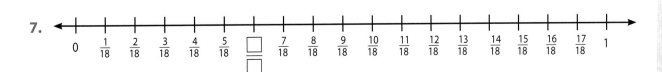

115

T R Y   I T

Sketch shapes or number lines to model the fractions. Then state whether or not the fractions are equivalent. Explain why or why not.

8. $\frac{4}{6}$ and $\frac{8}{12}$

9. $1\frac{2}{3}$ and $1\frac{2}{6}$

10. $2\frac{1}{2}$ and $2\frac{5}{8}$

Determine Equivalent Fractions (B)

Divide to Make Equivalent Fractions

Worked Examples

An equivalent fraction can have a denominator less than the denominator of the given fraction.

PROBLEM $\frac{15}{25} = \frac{?}{5}$

SOLUTION 1

1 Model $\frac{15}{25}$.

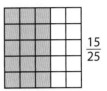

$\frac{15}{25}$

2 Divide the model to show 5 total parts instead of 25 total parts. Now 3 of the 5 total parts are shaded.

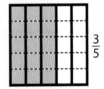

$\frac{3}{5}$

SOLUTION 2

1 Rewrite $\frac{15}{25} = \frac{?}{5}$ using the identity property of multiplication.

$$\frac{15}{25} = 1 \times \frac{?}{5}$$

2 Rewrite 1 as a fraction

$$\frac{15}{25} = \frac{a}{a} \times \frac{?}{5}$$

3 Determine the denominator of the fraction that has a value of 1. Think: 5 times what number equals 25? Or 25 divided by 5 equals what number?

$$\frac{15}{25} = \frac{a}{5} \times \frac{?}{5}$$

4 Complete the fraction equal to 1. The numerator must equal the denominator.

$$\frac{15}{25} = \frac{5}{5} \times \frac{?}{5}$$

5 Determine the numerator of the equivalent fraction. Think: 5 times what number equals 15? Or 15 divided by 5 equals what number?

$$\frac{15}{25} = \frac{5}{5} \times \frac{3}{5}$$

ANSWER $\frac{15}{25} = \frac{3}{5}$

LEARN

Determine the equivalent fraction.

1. $\dfrac{6}{10} = \dfrac{?}{5}$

2. $\dfrac{7}{21} = \dfrac{?}{3}$

3. $\dfrac{8}{16} = \dfrac{?}{4}$

4. $\dfrac{20}{24} = \dfrac{?}{6}$

5. $\dfrac{16}{20} = \dfrac{8}{?}$

6. $\dfrac{6}{12} = \dfrac{4}{?}$

7. $\dfrac{10}{15} = \dfrac{2}{?}$

8. $\dfrac{12}{18} = \dfrac{4}{?}$

LEARN

Compare Fractions (A)
Compare Fractions with Models

Worked Examples

You can use models to compare fractions. You can also use what you know about equivalent fractions.

PROBLEM Johnny and Ron each had the same kind of sandwich. Johnny ate $\frac{3}{5}$ of his sandwich. Ron ate $\frac{4}{10}$ of his sandwich. Who ate more of his sandwich?

SOLUTION 1 Model each fraction. Compare the shaded parts.

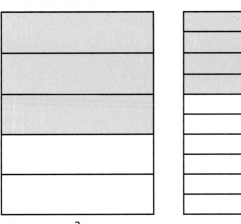

$$\frac{3}{5} \qquad > \qquad \frac{4}{10}$$

SOLUTION 2 Rewrite the fractions so they have the same denominator. Then compare the fractions.

$$\frac{3}{5} \times \frac{2}{2} = \frac{6}{10}$$

$$\frac{6}{10} > \frac{4}{10}, \text{ so } \frac{3}{5} > \frac{4}{10}$$

ANSWER Johnny ate more of his sandwich than Ron ate.

LEARN

Compare. Use >, <, or =.

1.
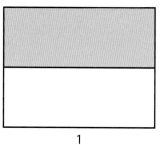

$$\frac{1}{2} \quad \underset{\_\_}{?} \quad \frac{4}{6}$$

2.
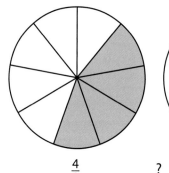

$$\frac{4}{9} \quad \underset{\_\_}{?} \quad \frac{2}{3}$$

3.
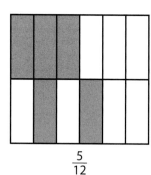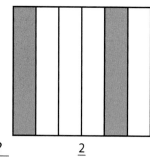

$$\frac{5}{12} \quad \underset{\_\_}{?} \quad \frac{2}{6}$$

4.
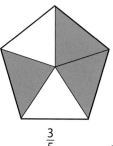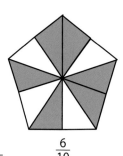

$$\frac{3}{5} \quad \underset{\_\_}{?} \quad \frac{6}{10}$$

Solve. Show your work

5. Serena and Rosa both had the same sized bedrooms. Serena covered $\frac{1}{4}$ of her bedroom floor with toys. Rosa covered $\frac{4}{12}$ of her bedroom floor with toys. Who covered a greater fraction of her bedroom floor with toys?

Compare Fractions (A)

Fraction Comparisons

Use sketches or number lines to model the fractions. Then compare.
Use $<$, $>$, or $=$.

1. $\frac{4}{10}$ __?__ $\frac{2}{5}$

2. $\frac{4}{6}$ __?__ $\frac{3}{9}$

3. $\frac{7}{12}$ __?__ $\frac{3}{4}$

4. $\frac{1}{2}$ __?__ $\frac{6}{10}$

Compare. Use $<$, $>$, or $=$.

5. $\frac{2}{3}$ __?__ $\frac{5}{6}$

6. $\frac{7}{10}$ __?__ $\frac{3}{5}$

Solve. Show your work.

7. Martina read $\frac{2}{4}$ of a novel on Monday. She read $\frac{3}{8}$ of the novel on Tuesday. On which day did Martina read more of her novel?

T R Y   I T

Compare Fractions (B)

Compare with Benchmark Fractions

Use <, >, or = to complete the statement. Explain how the model supports your answer.

1. $\dfrac{45}{100}$ __?__ $\dfrac{3}{5}$

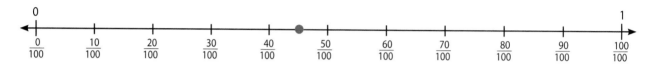

2. $\dfrac{5}{8}$ __?__ $\dfrac{7}{12}$

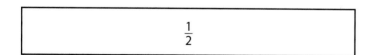

Use a benchmark to compare the fractions. Then use <, >, or = to complete the statement. Explain your answer.

3. $\dfrac{4}{6}$ __?__ $\dfrac{2}{4}$

4. $\dfrac{11}{12}$ __?__ $\dfrac{8}{9}$

TRY IT

Solve.

1. Mike and José shared a pan of macaroni and cheese. Mike ate $\frac{2}{5}$ of the macaroni and cheese. José ate $\frac{5}{10}$ of the macaroni and cheese.

    (a) Sketch a model to show how much of the macaroni and cheese each boy ate.

    (b) Compare $\frac{2}{5}$ and $\frac{5}{10}$ using $>$, $<$, or $=$.

    (c) Who ate less macaroni and cheese? Explain.

2. Paul exercised for 36 minutes. He spent $\frac{2}{6}$ of the time jogging. Beth exercised for 24 minutes. She spent $\frac{3}{8}$ of the time jogging.

    (a) Make a grid to show the total number of minutes that Paul exercised. Make a separate grid to show the total number of minutes that Beth exercised.

    (b) Shade the area of Paul's grid that represents how much time he spent jogging. Shade the area of Beth's grid that represents how much time she spent jogging.

    (c) Beth says that $\frac{3}{8} > \frac{2}{6}$, so she jogged for a longer amount of time than Paul did. Is Beth's reasoning correct? Use your models to explain why or why not.

3. A lap lane in a swimming pool has a red flag at each twelfth of a lap. The red flags are labeled with the letters A–M. The number line is a model of the lane.

    (a) The lap lane also has two blue flags that divide the lane into three $\frac{1}{3}$ lap distances. Under which letter flags do the blue flags belong on the number line? Explain.

    (b) Lanie swam to the red flag labeled I. Use three different fractions to name that distance.

T R Y   I T

Think Like a Mathematician Self-Check

4. State the actions and thinking you used during this lesson as a math learner.

Math Thinking and Actions
I made sense of problems by • Explaining to myself what a problem means and what it asks for • Using drawings or diagrams to represent a problem I was solving
I explained my math thinking clearly.
I tried out new ways to check if an answer is reasonable.
Other

TRY IT

Estimate Lengths

Estimate Line Segments

Worked Examples

You can refer to a dual-scale ruler to estimate line segments.

PROBLEM Estimate the length of the line segment to the nearest inch and to the nearest centimeter.

SOLUTION

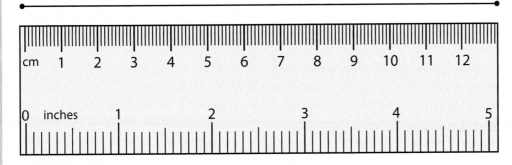

ANSWER about 5 inches, about 13 centimeters

Estimate the length of the line segment to the nearest inch and to the nearest centimeter.

1. •————————————•

2. •————————————————•

3. •———•

4. •——————————•

LEARN

Answer the question.

5. What is the length of the pencil in inches?

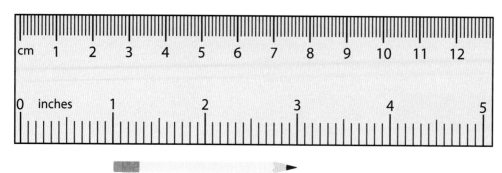

6. What is the length of the pencil in centimeters?

LEARN

Estimate Lengths

Length Estimation

Estimate the length of the object to the nearest inch.

1.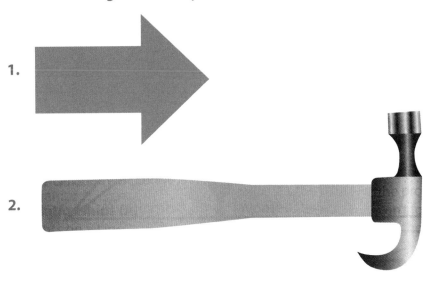

2.

Estimate the length of the object to the nearest centimeter.

3.

4.

Choose the answer.

5. Which is closest to 1 inch long?

   A. banana   B. spoon

   C. fork   D. grape

6. Which is closest to 1 centimeter long?

   A. raisin   B. lamp

   C. baseball bat   D. piano bench

TRY IT

Measurement in Story Problems (A)

Nature Story Problems

Worked Examples

To solve this story problem, read the problem, answer questions about the problem, and then solve the problem.

PROBLEM   A thirsty Asian elephant can drink 59 gallons of water.

How many gallons can 3 thirsty Asian elephants drink?

What operation can you use?

What number sentence can you use to solve the problem?

SOLUTION   You know 1 Asian elephant can drink 59 gallons of water. To find how many gallons 3 Asian elephants can drink, you multiply.

$3 \times 59 = ?$

ANSWER   multiply; $3 \times 59 = ?$; 177 gallons

Read the problem, answer questions about the problem, and then solve the problem.

1. Baby camels, called calves, grow to full size in about 6 years. Suppose 5 adult camels weigh 5,000 pounds altogether and they each weigh the same amount.

   How much does 1 camel weigh?

   What operation can you use?

   What number sentence can you use to solve the problem?

LEARN

Solve.

2. A blue whale calf can drink 128 gallons of milk per day.
   There are 4 quarts in 1 gallon.

   How many quarts of milk are in 128 gallons?

   How many quarts of milk can 3 blue whale calves drink in 1 day?

3. Adult humpback whales can eat 3,000 pounds of food a day.

   How many pounds of food can 12 humpback whales
   eat in a day? There are 16 ounces in 1 pound.

   How many ounces of food can 1 humpback whale eat in a day?

4. A line of ants is 980 millimeters long. If each ant is 7 millimeters long,
   how many ants are in the line?

5. Carpenter ants live outside in mountains as high as 9,000 feet.
   There are 3 feet in 1 yard.

   How many yards are in 9,000 feet?

LEARN

Measurement in Story Problems (A)

Measurement Story Problems

Solve.

1. Matt feeds his dog 6 pounds of food a week. There are 16 ounces in a pound. How many ounces of food does Matt feed his dog each week?

2. Sound travels about 1,000 feet in 1 second. About how far will the noise from thunder travel in 5 seconds?

3. A store has 220 yards of checked fabric that sells for $11 a yard. If the store sells all of the checked fabric, how much money will the store take in?

4. Justine made 2,000 milliliters of chicken soup. She divides it into 8 equal portions. How many milliliters are in each portion of soup?

5. A bald eagle can eat about 4,000 grams of fish in a week. There are 1,000 grams in a kilogram. About how many kilograms of fish can a bald eagle eat in a week?

Choose the answer.

6. Kevin charged $6 to wash a car. He washed 12 cars. How much money did he earn?

   A. $94   B. $72   C. $18   D. $2

7. Thirty cyclists each drank 2 pints of water. How many pints of water did they drink altogether?

   A. 90 pints   B. 60 pints   C. 30 pints   D. 15 pints

8. Devan uses 4 feet of wood to make a picture frame. There are 12 inches in a foot. How many inches of wood does Devan use to make a picture frame?

   A. 12 inches   B. 16 inches   C. 24 inches   D. 48 inches

9. Lyn spent $54 for 9 plants for her backyard. If each plant costs the same amount, how much did each plant cost?

   A. $6   B. $8   C. $456   D. $486

TRY IT

Measurement in Story Problems (B)

Everyday Measurements

Worked Examples

You can multiply or divide to solve story problems with equal measures. The operation you choose depends on what the problem asks you to find.

PROBLEM A group of 8 hikers wore backpacks of equal weight. The backpacks had a total weight of 128 pounds.

What was the weight of each backpack?

SOLUTION

Do you know the total, or do you have to find it? ⟶ I know the total.

What operation will you use to solve the problem? ⟶ division

What is the solution to the problem? ⟶ 128 total pounds ÷ 8 hikers = 16 pounds per backpack

ANSWER 16 pounds

Solve.

1. A large can of tomato soup has a mass of 538 grams. What is the mass of 2 cans of soup?

   Do you know the total, or do you have to find it?

   What operation will you use to solve the problem?

   What is the solution to the problem?

LEARN

2. Tony's train layout has 216 inches of straight track. The track comes in 9-inch sections. How many sections of straight track does Tony's layout have?

   Do you know the total, or do you have to find it?

   What operation will you use to solve the problem?

   What is the solution to the problem?

3. Natalie ran in a 5-mile race. One mile equals 5,280 feet. What is the total number of feet that Natalie ran?

   Do you know the total, or do you have to find it?

   What operation will you use to solve the problem?

   What is the solution to the problem?

4. At a hot-air balloon festival, 300 students make hot-air balloons from tissue paper. Each student uses 30 sheets of colored tissue paper for one balloon. How many sheets of tissue paper will the students use?

   Do you know the total, or do you have to find it?

   What operation will you use to solve the problem?

   What is the solution to the problem?

5. Juan recycles the ink cartridges from his computer printer. He gets a $3 coupon for each recycled cartridge. Juan received $189 worth of coupons in 2 years. How many cartridges did he recycle in that time?

   Do you know the total, or do you have to find it?

   What operation will you use to solve the problem?

   What is the solution to the problem?

LEARN

Measurement in Story Problems (B)

Two-Step Measurement Problems

Worked Examples

Sometimes it takes two steps to solve a story problem. The operations you choose depend on what the problem asks you to find.

PROBLEM 1   Maria made 24 muffins. She used 3 pounds of flour to make them. How many ounces of flour were in each muffin?

SOLUTION

What facts are given? $\longrightarrow$ There are 24 muffins. It took 3 pounds of flour to make them.

What operations will you use to solve the problem? $\longrightarrow$ First I will multiply to find how many ounces of flour Maria used.

Then I will divide to find how many ounces of flour are in each muffin.

What is the solution to the problem? $\longrightarrow$ 16 ounces $\times$ 3 pounds = 48 ounces of flour

48 ounces of flour $\div$ 24 muffins = 2 ounces of flour per muffin

ANSWER   There are 2 ounces of flour in each muffin.

L E A R N

Solve

1. Jack has 12 feet of wood. He cuts it into 4 equal pieces. How many inches long is each piece? There are 12 inches in a foot.

   What facts are given?

   What operations will you use to solve?

   What is the answer?

2. Crystal's aquarium holds 25 gallons of water. There are 22 gallons of water in the aquarium. How many more quarts of water will it take to fill it? There are 4 quarts in a gallon.

   What facts are given?

   What operations will you use to solve?

   What is the answer?

3. Jeremy bought 5 pounds of dog food. He divided it into 8 containers. How many ounces of dog food are in each container? There are 16 ounces in a pound.

   What facts are given?

   What operations will you use to solve?

   What is the answer?

4. Rachel glued two pieces of wood together to make one 4-foot-long piece of wood. One of the pieces she glued was 30 inches long. How many inches long was the other piece of wood? There are 12 inches in a foot.

   What facts are given?

   What operations will you use to solve?

   What is the answer?

5. Mel bought 4 kilograms of potting soil. He put the same amount of soil into 8 different flower pots. How many grams of soil did Mel put in each flower pot? There are 1,000 grams in a kilogram.

   What facts are given?

   What operations will you use to solve?

   What is the answer?

LEARN

Measurement in Story Problems (B)

Equal Measures

Solve.

1. A telephone worker has 1,407 feet of telephone wire. He completes 7 jobs and uses the same amount of wire for each job.

   How many feet of wire does the telephone worker use for each job?

2. A bottle of shampoo holds 945 milliliters. Grace uses 3 milliliters of shampoo each time she washes her hair.

   How many times can Grace wash her hair before the shampoo runs out?

3. The hockey team wants to buy sew-on patches for the players. The patches cost $5 each.

   How many patches can the team buy if it spends $150?

4. John filled a watering can with 4 gallons of water. He used 14 quarts to water his flowers.

   How many quarts of water were left in the watering can? There are 4 quarts in a gallon.

Choose the answer.

5. Ethan is placing tiles along the edge of a countertop. Each tile is 8 centimeters long.

   How many tiles will Ethan need if the countertop is 144 centimeters long?

   A. 18 tiles

   B. 12 tiles

   C. 18 centimeters

   D. 1,152 centimeters

6. Joe's company bought 48 golf umbrellas with the company logo.

   If each umbrella cost $16, how much did Joe's company spend on them?

   A. $3

   B. $4

   C. $640

   D. $768

7. Animated movies on DVD are on sale for $9 each. Alexis has $135 to spend.

   How many DVDs can Alexis buy?

   A. 15 DVDs

   B. 19 DVDs

   C. $15

   D. 1,215 DVDs

8. Michelle has 4 kites. She used 63 feet of string on each kite.

   How many yards of string did Michelle use on all 4 kites? There are 3 feet in a yard.

   A. 21 yards

   B. 74 yards

   C. 84 yards

   D. 256 yards

TRY IT

Using Metric Units

Solve.

1. Kim drank 5,000 milliliters of juice in 5 days. She drank the same amount of juice each day. How milliliters of juice did she drink each day?

   (a) What are you asked to find?

   (b) Will you divide or multiply to find the answer? Explain.

   (c) Write an equation to solve the problem. Then solve the problem.

2. Mateo bought 7 kilograms of mulch for his garden. How many grams of mulch did he buy?

   (a) What conversion number sentence can you use to solve the problem?

   (b) Are you changing from smaller units to larger units or larger units to smaller units? Explain.

   (c) Should you multiply or divide to solve the problem? Explain.

   (d) Write an equation to solve the problem. Then solve the problem.

3. Stan bought 700 centimeters of cloth to make banners for his school's baseball team. How many meters of cloth did he buy?

   (a) What conversion number sentence can you use to solve the problem?

   (b) Are you changing from smaller units to larger units or larger units to smaller units? Explain.

   (c) Should you multiply or divide to solve the problem? Explain.

   (d) Write an equation to solve the problem. Then solve the problem

4. Rachel has 6 meters of ribbon. She uses 150 centimeters of ribbon to make a bow. How many bows can Rachel make from the ribbon?

   (a) How many steps do you need to solve this problem? Explain.

   (b) What operations will you use? Explain.

   (c) Solve the problem. Show your work.

Think Like a Mathematician Self-Check

5. State the actions and thinking you used during this lesson as a math learner.

Math Thinking and Actions
I made sense of problems by • Explaining to myself what a problem means and what it asks for • Using drawings or diagrams to represent a problem I was solving
I explained my math thinking clearly.
I tried out new ways to check if an answer is reasonable.
Other

TRY IT

Add and Subtract Fractions (A)

Take Apart Mixed Numbers

Worked Examples

You can express mixed numbers as sums and as improper fractions.

PROBLEM 1 Express $1\frac{3}{5}$ as the sum of unit fractions.

SOLUTION Model the mixed number on a number line.

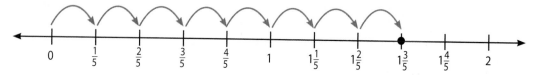

Count the jumps. Each jump on the number line has a distance of $\frac{1}{5}$.

ANSWER $1\frac{3}{5} = \frac{1}{5} + \frac{1}{5} + \frac{1}{5} + \frac{1}{5} + \frac{1}{5} + \frac{1}{5} + \frac{1}{5} + \frac{1}{5}$

PROBLEM 2 Express $1\frac{3}{5}$ as a sum in two different ways.

SOLUTION Group the unit fractions differently to show equivalent sums.

ANSWER $1\frac{3}{5} = \left(\frac{1}{5} + \frac{1}{5} + \frac{1}{5} + \frac{1}{5}\right) + \left(\frac{1}{5} + \frac{1}{5} + \frac{1}{5} + \frac{1}{5}\right) = \frac{4}{5} + \frac{4}{5}$

$1\frac{3}{5} = \left(\frac{1}{5} + \frac{1}{5}\right) + \frac{1}{5} + \left(\frac{1}{5} + \frac{1}{5} + \frac{1}{5} + \frac{1}{5} + \frac{1}{5}\right) = \frac{2}{5} + \frac{1}{5} + \frac{5}{5}$

PROBLEM 3 Express $1\frac{3}{5}$ as an improper fraction.

SOLUTION Combine the unit fractions to determine the total number of fifths.

ANSWER $1\frac{3}{5} = \frac{1}{5} + \frac{1}{5} + \frac{1}{5} + \frac{1}{5} + \frac{1}{5} + \frac{1}{5} + \frac{1}{5} + \frac{1}{5} = \frac{8}{5}$

L E A R N

Solve. Show your work.

1. The number line shows the mixed number $1\frac{1}{2}$.

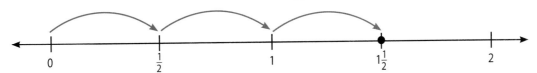

(a) Express $1\frac{1}{2}$ as the sum of unit fractions.

(b) Express $1\frac{1}{2}$ as a sum in a way that is different from but is equivalent to the sum in Part (a).

(c) Express $1\frac{1}{2}$ as an improper fraction.

2. The model shows the mixed number $2\frac{2}{3}$.

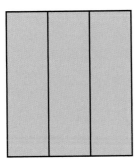 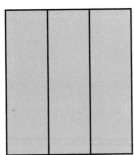 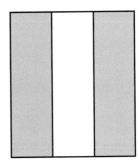

(a) Express $2\frac{2}{3}$ as the sum of unit fractions.

(b) Express $2\frac{2}{3}$ as a sum in two ways that are different from but are equivalent to the sum in Part (a).

(c) Express $2\frac{2}{3}$ as an improper fraction.

LEARN

Add and Subtract Fractions (A)

Different Ways to Take Apart

Express the fraction as the sum of unit fractions. Use a sketch or number line to explain your reasoning.

1. $\frac{4}{6}$

2. $\frac{7}{10}$

Express the mixed number as the sum of unit fractions. Then express it as an improper fraction. Use a sketch or number line to explain your reasoning.

3. $1\frac{1}{8}$

4. $2\frac{2}{4}$

Express the fraction or mixed number as a sum in two different ways.

5. $\frac{11}{12}$

6. $3\frac{1}{2}$

7. $\frac{6}{6}$

Solve.

8. Amber says that $\frac{2}{3} = \frac{1}{2} + \frac{1}{2} + \frac{1}{2}$. Is Amber correct? Explain why or why not.

TRY IT

Add and Subtract Fractions (B)

Add, Subtract, and Simplify

Worked Examples

You can use fraction strips to add, subtract, and simplify fractions.

PROBLEM 1 You need $\frac{1}{6}$ cup of milk to make one recipe. You need $\frac{3}{6}$ cup to make another recipe. How much milk do you need to make both recipes? Use fraction strips to find the sum. Then write the problem and show your work.

SOLUTION

1 Begin with one $\frac{1}{6}$ piece on the fraction strip.

$\frac{1}{6}$	$\frac{1}{6}$	$\frac{1}{6}$	$\frac{1}{6}$	$\frac{1}{6}$	$\frac{1}{6}$

2 Add three $\frac{1}{6}$ pieces to the one $\frac{1}{6}$ piece. There are four $\frac{1}{6}$ pieces, so $\frac{1}{6} + \frac{3}{6} = \frac{4}{6}$.

$\frac{1}{6}$	$\frac{1}{6}$	$\frac{1}{6}$	$\frac{1}{6}$	$\frac{1}{6}$	$\frac{1}{6}$

3 Simplify the sum if possible. Look for one fraction piece or two or more identical pieces that are each larger than a $\frac{1}{6}$ piece but combine to be the same length as $\frac{4}{6}$. A strip with two $\frac{1}{3}$ pieces is the same length as four $\frac{1}{6}$ pieces, so $\frac{4}{6} = \frac{2}{3}$.

$\frac{1}{3}$	$\frac{1}{3}$	$\frac{1}{3}$

$$\begin{array}{r} \frac{1}{6} \\ + \frac{3}{6} \\ \hline \frac{4}{6} = \frac{2}{3} \end{array}$$

ANSWER You need $\frac{4}{6}$, or $\frac{2}{3}$, cup of milk to make both recipes.

LEARN

PROBLEM 2 A black tropical fish is $\frac{5}{8}$ inch long. A yellow tropical fish is $\frac{3}{8}$ inch long. How much longer is the black tropical fish than the yellow tropical fish? Use fraction strips to find the difference. Then write the problem and show your work.

SOLUTION

1 Begin with five $\frac{1}{8}$ pieces on the fraction strip. Place three $\frac{1}{8}$ pieces below the five pieces. Compare the shaded parts of the fraction strips.

2 Subtract by comparing $\frac{5}{8}$ to $\frac{3}{8}$ or take away three matching pairs of $\frac{1}{8}$ pieces. The difference, or $\frac{2}{8}$, is left.

3 Simplify the difference if possible. Because one $\frac{1}{4}$ piece is the same length as two $\frac{1}{8}$ pieces, the fraction $\frac{1}{4}$ equals $\frac{2}{8}$.

ANSWER The black tropical fish is $\frac{2}{8}$, or $\frac{1}{4}$, inch longer than the yellow tropical fish.

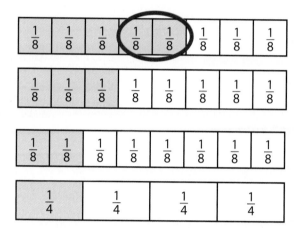

$$\begin{array}{r} \frac{5}{8} \\ -\frac{3}{8} \\ \hline \frac{2}{8} = \frac{1}{4} \end{array}$$

Solve. Use fraction strips to add or subtract. Write the answer in simplest form.

1. Toby and his father walk $\frac{2}{6}$ mile to the store. Then they walk $\frac{1}{6}$ mile to the library.

   How far do they walk in all?

2. John prints a program for the community theater play. The text takes up $\frac{2}{5}$ of the page. The art takes up $\frac{1}{5}$ of the page.

   How much of the page has text or art?

3. Maria has $\frac{7}{8}$ yard of fabric. She cuts $\frac{4}{8}$ yard and uses it for a craft.

   How much of the fabric is left?

4. Molly mixes trail mix and raisins to make a snack. She makes $\frac{5}{6}$ cup of the snack. She uses $\frac{4}{6}$ cup trail mix.

   How many cups of raisins does Molly use?

LEARN

Add and Subtract Fractions (B)

Use Sketches to Add and Subtract

Worked Examples

You can make sketches to help you solve story problems that involve addition and subtraction of fractions.

PROBLEM 1 Joshua has a board that is $\frac{3}{4}$ yard long. He cuts off $\frac{1}{4}$ yard. How long is the board now? Sketch pictures on grid paper to find the difference.

SOLUTION

1 Sketch a rectangle to show $\frac{3}{4}$.

Below that rectangle, sketch another rectangle the same size that shows $\frac{1}{4}$.

2 Compare the shaded parts of the grids to subtract.

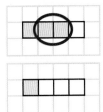

Since $\frac{3}{4}$ is $\frac{2}{4}$ longer than $\frac{1}{4}$,

$$\frac{3}{4} - \frac{1}{4} = \frac{2}{4}.$$

3 Decide if you can simplify $\frac{2}{4}$. Sketch $\frac{2}{4}$ on a new rectangle and sketch a blank rectangle the same size below it. Try to find a fraction larger than $\frac{1}{4}$ that is the same length as $\frac{2}{4}$ and shade it. Since $\frac{2}{4}$ and $\frac{1}{2}$ cover the same fraction of the rectangle, $\frac{2}{4}$ in simplest form is $\frac{1}{2}$.

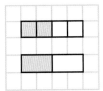

4 Show your work and write the solution.

$$\begin{array}{r} \frac{3}{4} \\ -\frac{1}{4} \\ \hline \frac{2}{4} = \frac{1}{2} \end{array}$$

ANSWER The board is $\frac{2}{4}$, or $\frac{1}{2}$, yard long.

LEARN

PROBLEM 2 Gia read $\frac{1}{6}$ of the book on Monday. She read $\frac{4}{6}$ of the book on Tuesday. What fraction of the book has Gia read in all?

SOLUTION

1 Sketch a rectangle to show $\frac{1}{6}$.

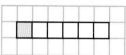

Below that rectangle, sketch another rectangle the same size that shows $\frac{4}{6}$.

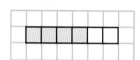

2 Count sixths on both rectangles.

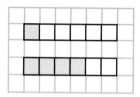

There are 5 sixths in all, or $\frac{5}{6}$.

3 Sketch the answer $\frac{5}{6}$ on a new rectangle and draw a blank rectangle below it the same size. Since you cannot sketch a fraction equivalent to $\frac{5}{6}$ using a larger fraction, $\frac{5}{6}$ is in simplest form.

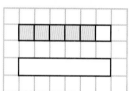

4 Show your work and write the solution.

$$\begin{array}{r} \frac{1}{6} \\ +\ \frac{4}{6} \\ \hline \frac{5}{6} \end{array}$$

ANSWER Gia read $\frac{5}{6}$ of her book.

Solve. Sketch a picture to add or subtract. Write the answer in simplest form.

1. Heather has a ribbon that is $\frac{2}{3}$ foot long. She gives $\frac{1}{3}$ foot of the ribbon to her friend.

   How much ribbon does Heather have left?

2. In an art studio, $\frac{2}{4}$ of the construction paper is red and $\frac{1}{4}$ of the construction paper is blue. The rest of the paper is white.

   What fraction of the pack of paper is red or blue?

3. A pitcher has $\frac{2}{6}$ gallon of orange juice and $\frac{2}{6}$ gallon of pineapple juice.

   How much juice is in the pitcher in all?

4. June has $\frac{5}{10}$ meter of yarn. She use $\frac{3}{10}$ meter for a project.

   How much of the yarn is left?

Add and Subtract Fractions (C)

Mixed Number Addition and Subtraction

Worked Examples

You can use number lines for addition and subtraction that involves mixed numbers and improper fractions.

PROBLEM 1 Ron bought $\frac{5}{6}$ yard of canvas for a camp project. He did not have enough canvas, so he bought another $\frac{2}{6}$ yard of canvas. How much canvas did Ron buy?

SOLUTION

1 Number Line 1: Sketch $\frac{5}{6}$.

2 Number Line 2: Sketch $\frac{2}{6}$.

3 Number Line 3: Begin at $\frac{5}{6}$ and sketch $\frac{2}{6}$ to add $\frac{5}{6} + \frac{2}{6}$.

4 Number Line 4: Simplify the answer, if necessary. Because $\frac{7}{6}$ is an improper fraction, change it to a mixed number to simplify it.
Look at Number Line 4 to find the mixed number.

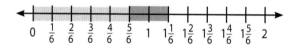

ANSWER Ron bought $\frac{7}{6}$, or $1\frac{1}{6}$, yards of canvas.

$$\frac{5}{6}$$
$$+ \frac{2}{6}$$
$$\overline{\frac{7}{6}} = 1\frac{1}{6}$$

LEARN

PROBLEM 2 There are $1\frac{2}{3}$ boxes of graham crackers. To make campfire snacks, the campers use $1\frac{1}{3}$ boxes. What fraction of a box of graham crackers is left?

SOLUTION

1 Number Line 1: Sketch $1\frac{2}{3}$.

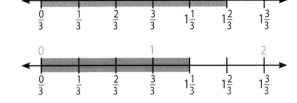

2 Number Line 2: Sketch $1\frac{1}{3}$.

3 Number Line 3: To subtract $1\frac{1}{3}$ from $1\frac{2}{3}$, change $1\frac{1}{3}$ to an improper fraction. Look at Number Line 3 to find the improper fraction equivalent to $1\frac{1}{3}$.

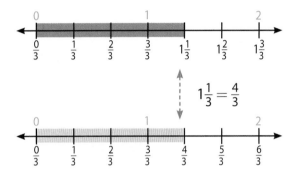

$$1\frac{1}{3} = \frac{4}{3}$$

4 Number Line 4: Jump back $\frac{4}{3}$ to subtract $1\frac{1}{3}$ from $1\frac{2}{3}$. $1\frac{2}{3} - 1\frac{1}{3} = \frac{1}{3}$, and $\frac{1}{3}$ is in simplest form.

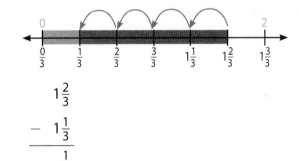

$$
\begin{array}{r}
1\frac{2}{3} \\
-\ 1\frac{1}{3} \\
\hline
\frac{1}{3}
\end{array}
$$

ANSWER There is $\frac{1}{3}$ box of graham crackers left.

LEARN

Solve. Use number lines to add or subtract. Write the answer in simplest form.

1. Serena swam $1\frac{1}{2}$ miles on Saturday and $1\frac{1}{2}$ miles on Sunday. How far did Serena swim altogether?

2. Alexander had $1\frac{1}{4}$ cups of raisins. He and his friends ate $\frac{2}{4}$ cup. How much of the raisins were left?

3. The cookie recipe uses $1\frac{1}{3}$ cups of white sugar and $\frac{1}{3}$ cup of brown sugar. How much sugar is in the cookie recipe altogether?

Solve. Show your work. Write the answer in simplest form.

4. A recipe for a wedding cake calls for $5\frac{3}{4}$ cups flour. The cake baker has $4\frac{1}{4}$ cups flour. How much more flour does the baker need to make the wedding cake?

5. A cross-country running race is $3\frac{1}{10}$ kilometers long. Erin completed two cross-country races this month. How many total kilometers did Erin race this month?

6. Jonas measured $2\frac{1}{4}$ cups of water to use for cooking rice. He then realized he needed only 2 cups. How much extra water did he measure?

LEARN

Add and Subtract Fractions (D)

More Tenths and Hundredths

Determine the value of *a*. Sketch a model to explain your reasoning.

1. $\frac{2}{10} = \frac{a}{100}$

2. $\frac{7}{10} = \frac{a}{100}$

Explain how the model represents the expression. Then find the sum.

3. $\frac{3}{10} + \frac{6}{100}$

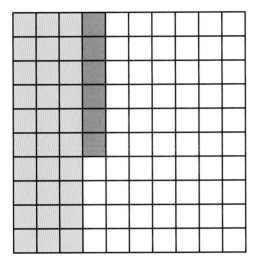

4. $\frac{8}{10} + \frac{34}{100}$

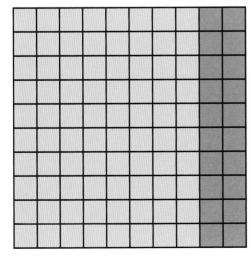 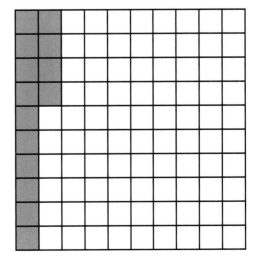

TRY IT

Add.

5. $\frac{5}{10} + \frac{1}{100}$

6. $\frac{8}{100} + \frac{1}{10}$

7. $\frac{4}{10} + \frac{31}{100}$

8. $\frac{9}{10} + \frac{22}{100}$

9. $3\frac{6}{100} + 2\frac{7}{10}$

10. $1\frac{30}{100} + \frac{8}{10}$

Solve. Show your work.

11. A decade is $\frac{1}{10}$ of a century. A year is $\frac{1}{100}$ of a century. Joseph is 6 decades and 7 years old. What fraction of a century has Joseph been alive?

TRY IT

Make Line Plots

Create Line Plots with Fractions

Worked Examples

You can create a line plot to picture a group of values.

PROBLEM 1 The set of values are the time intervals, in minutes, between eruptions at Old Faithful Geyser in Yellowstone National Park. The time intervals are rounded to the nearest 5 minutes. Make a line plot for this data set.

$$65, 55, 55, 45, 80, 45, 65, 70, 60, 55, 90, 45, 60, 40, 55$$

SOLUTION

1 Look through the data set and find the greatest value and the least value. Create a number line and place the least value on the far left and the greatest value on the far right. (Your number line may extend beyond the least and greatest values in the data set.) Then place tick marks and labels at regular spaces between the least and greatest values, at intervals of 5.

```
←——+——+——+——+——+——+——+——+——+——+——+——→
   40  45  50  55  60  65  70  75  80  85  90
```

2 Label the line plot with a title and a label for the values on the number line.

3 Place a mark above the number line according the first value, 65.

Time Intervals Between Old Faithful Eruptions

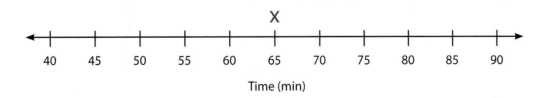

Time (min)

L E A R N

4 Place marks according to the rest of the data values in the set. If you have more than one mark at a location, arrange your marks so that they line up both across from each other and up and down.

ANSWER

Time Intervals Between Old Faithful Eruptions

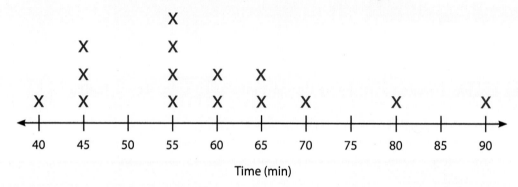

Time (min)

PROBLEM 2 A machine operator in a factory is trying to adjust a machine to make sure that the machine is making parts that are the correct weight. She has collected the following weights for the parts, in ounces. Create a line plot for this data set.

$$\frac{1}{4}, \frac{1}{8}, \frac{1}{2}, \frac{1}{8}, \frac{3}{8}, \frac{5}{8}, \frac{3}{8}, \frac{1}{8}, \frac{1}{4}, \frac{1}{4}, \frac{3}{4}, \frac{3}{8}, \frac{1}{4}, \frac{1}{2}, \frac{3}{8}, \frac{1}{4}, \frac{3}{8}, \frac{1}{2}, \frac{5}{8}, \frac{3}{8}$$

SOLUTION

1 Create the number line. In this case, since all the values are between 0 and 1, use 0 and 1 as the start and end values for the line plot. Then make tick marks at every one-eighth of an ounce. Remember that some of the values of the eighths will need to be put in simplest form, such as $\frac{2}{8} = \frac{1}{4}$.

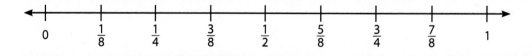

L E A R N

② Give the line plot a title and create a label for the numbers. Place a mark for each value in the data set. Make sure the number of marks matches the number of values. Remember to arrange your marks so that they line up both across from each other and up and down.

ANSWER

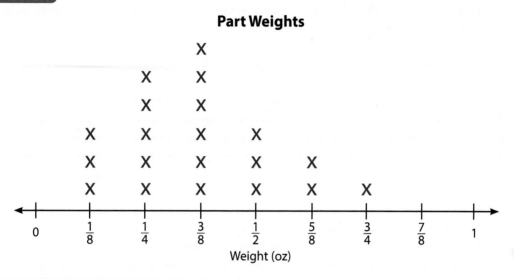

Create a line plot for the data set. For the data sets that provide information about the data, write a title for the line plot and provide an appropriate label with units for the numbers.

1. Students ran 100-yard sprints in gym class. Here are their individual times in seconds: 12, 15, 13, 15, 18, 13, 12, 11, 15, 14, 19, 11, 12, 15, 14.

2. $0, \frac{1}{5}, \frac{2}{5}, \frac{1}{5}, 0, \frac{3}{5}, 1, \frac{3}{5}, \frac{1}{5}, \frac{2}{5}, \frac{1}{5}, \frac{4}{5}, 0, \frac{3}{5}, \frac{4}{5}$

3. $\frac{1}{6}, \frac{1}{3}, \frac{1}{2}, \frac{1}{3}, \frac{1}{6}, \frac{1}{2}, \frac{2}{3}, \frac{1}{6}, \frac{2}{3}, \frac{1}{6}$

4. Insects were captured and measured in a field. The following data show their lengths in inches: $\frac{1}{10}, \frac{2}{5}, \frac{3}{10}, \frac{1}{10}, \frac{3}{10}, \frac{1}{2}, \frac{2}{5}, \frac{7}{10}, \frac{1}{10}, \frac{2}{5}, \frac{3}{10}, \frac{1}{5}, \frac{2}{5}, \frac{1}{2}, \frac{3}{10}.$

L E A R N

Make Line Plots

Use Line Plots with Fractions

You can use operations on the values presented in a line plot to answer questions about the data set.

- A machine operator in a factory is trying to adjust a machine to make sure the machine is making parts that are the correct weight. She has recorded the weights, in ounces, of several parts, and has displayed those data values in the line plot.

Part Weights

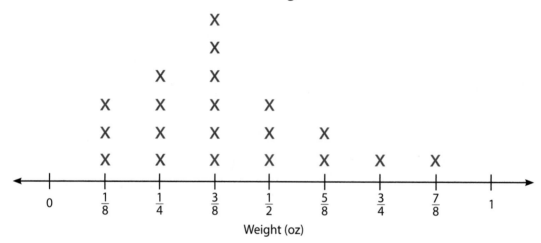

Weight (oz)

PROBLEM 1 What is the difference between the greatest value and the least value in the data set?

SOLUTION

1 Identify the least and greatest values in the data set.

least: $\frac{1}{8}$ greatest: $\frac{7}{8}$

2 Find the difference by subtracting.

$\frac{7}{8} - \frac{1}{8} = \frac{6}{8}$

3 Simplify the answer.

$\frac{6}{8} = \frac{6 \div 2}{8 \div 2} = \frac{3}{4}$

ANSWER $\frac{3}{4}$ oz

LEARN

PROBLEM 2 What is the sum of the three least weights?

SOLUTION The three least weights are $\frac{1}{8}$, $\frac{1}{8}$, and $\frac{1}{8}$. Find the sum.

$$\frac{1}{8} + \frac{1}{8} + \frac{1}{8} = \frac{3}{8}$$

ANSWER $\frac{3}{8}$ oz

PROBLEM 3 What is the sum of all the weights that occur the most?

SOLUTION The weight of $\frac{3}{8}$ occurs the most. Count the number of weights at $\frac{3}{8}$. There are six weights of $\frac{3}{8}$, so find the sum and simplify the answer.

$$\frac{3}{8} + \frac{3}{8} + \frac{3}{8} + \frac{3}{8} + \frac{3}{8} + \frac{3}{8} = \frac{18}{8}$$

$$\frac{18 \div 2}{8 \div 2} = \frac{9}{4}$$

ANSWER $\frac{9}{4}$ oz

PROBLEM 4 How many of the weights are at the value of $\frac{5}{8}$ or greater?

SOLUTION There are two weights of $\frac{5}{8}$, one weight of $\frac{3}{4}$, and one weight of $\frac{7}{8}$.

ANSWER There are four weights of $\frac{5}{8}$ or greater.

PROBLEM 5 What fraction of the total number of weights is at the value of $\frac{5}{8}$ or greater?

SOLUTION

There are four weights of $\frac{5}{8}$ or greater and 20 weights total. As a fraction, it is

$$\frac{\text{\# of weights at } \frac{5}{8} \text{ or greater}}{\text{total \# of weights}} = \frac{4}{20}; \text{ simplified: } \frac{4}{20} = \frac{1}{5}.$$

ANSWER $\frac{1}{5}$

LEARN

For each line plot, answer the questions. Simplify all fraction answers.

(a) What is the difference between the greatest value and the least value in the data set?

(b) What is the sum of the greatest value and the least value in the data set?

(c) What is the sum of all the data values that occur the most?

(d) What fraction of all the values occurs at the least value?

1.

2.

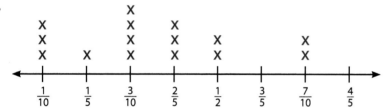

3.

L E A R N

Different Ways to Write Products

Different Products

Answer the question.

1. Sara knew that $18 \times 2 = 36$. What is another way to write 36 as a product of factors?

2. How can you write 50 as a product of only prime numbers?

3. Write three number sentences in which each product is equal to 40.

Choose the answer.

4. Jerome had 12 squares. He made this rectangle.

   Which other rectangle could he make with 12 squares?

   A.

   B.

   C.

   D.

5. Jackson had 12 squares. He made this rectangle.

   Which other rectangle could he make with 12 squares?

   A. 2 unit × 12 unit rectangle

   B. 2 unit × 6 unit rectangle

   C. 3 unit × 6 unit rectangle

   D. 8 unit × 2 unit rectangle

6. Regan knew that $60 = 10 \times 6$. Which expression also equals 60?

   A. 4×20 B. 5×12

   C. 8×8 D. 9×6

7. Tom wrote $10 \times 10 = 100$. Which equation is also correct?

   A. $2 \times 40 = 100$ B. $4 \times 15 = 100$

   C. $5 \times 20 = 100$ D. $8 \times 12 = 100$

8. Which equations equal 12? Choose **two**.

   A. $1 \times 11 = 12$ B. $2 \times 6 = 12$

   C. $4 \times 4 = 12$ D. $3 \times 4 = 12$

9. Which equations equal 24? Choose **two**.

   A. $1 \times 24 = 24$ B. $2 \times 8 = 24$

   C. $4 \times 4 = 24$ D. $2 \times 12 = 24$

10. Which is another way to write $5 \times 12 = 60$?

    A. $60 = 2 \times 2 \times 3 \times 5$ B. $60 = 2 \times 5 \times 5$

    C. $60 = 2 \times 2 \times 12$ D. $60 = 5 \times 10 + 2$

TRY IT

Fraction and Whole Number Products (A)

Multiply and Simplify

Worked Examples

You can multiply a fraction by a whole number by using a model and by using an algorithm, or a step-by-step process.

PROBLEM A recipe calls for $\frac{1}{3}$ cup of water. Naomi is making 9 times the recipe. How much water does she need?

SOLUTION 1 The model shows that every 3 thirds equals 1. So 6 thirds equals 2, and 9 thirds equals 3.

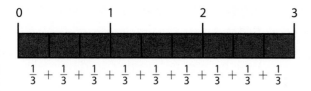

$$\frac{1}{3} + \frac{1}{3} + \frac{1}{3} + \frac{1}{3} + \frac{1}{3} + \frac{1}{3} + \frac{1}{3} + \frac{1}{3} + \frac{1}{3}$$

SOLUTION 2 $9 \times \frac{1}{3} = \frac{9 \times 1}{3} = \frac{9}{3} = 3$

ANSWER Naomi needs 3 cups of water.

Write a multiplication expression to represent the problem. Then solve.

1. Each folded towel takes up $\frac{1}{5}$ of a shelf. How many shelves are needed for 20 folded towels?

2. Each member of a relay team runs $\frac{1}{4}$ mile. There are 4 members of the relay team. What total distance does the relay team run?

3. Every morning, Rob eats $\frac{1}{2}$ of a banana for breakfast. How many bananas does Rob eat in 50 mornings?

4. Every day, the animal shelter uses $\frac{1}{7}$ of a large bag of dog food to feed all the dogs. How many bags of dog food does the animal shelter use in 2 weeks? (1 week = 7 days)

LEARN

Fraction and Whole Number Products (B)

Multiply Fractions and Whole Numbers

Worked Examples

You can use a model and use an algorithm, or a step-by-step process, to multiply a fraction by a whole number.

PROBLEM One lap around a path is $\frac{5}{8}$ mile. Jarell jogged 3 laps. How far did Jarell jog?

SOLUTION 1 Model the problem using repeated addition on a number line.

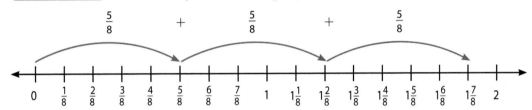

$$\frac{5}{8} + \frac{5}{8} + \frac{5}{8} = \frac{15}{8} = 1\frac{7}{8}$$

SOLUTION 2 Model the problem with a multiplication expression. Multiply the numerator of the fraction factor by the whole-number factor.

$$3 \times \frac{5}{8} = \frac{3 \times 5}{8} = \frac{15}{8} = 1\frac{7}{8}$$

ANSWER Jarell jogged $1\frac{7}{8}$ miles.

Solve. Show your work.

1. The 4 children each ate $\frac{7}{10}$ of an apple for a snack. How many total apples did the children eat altogether?

2. Sonya is cooking for a banquet. She wants to make 20 times the amount of green beans that a recipe makes. The recipe calls for $\frac{9}{2}$ cups of green beans. How many cups of green beans should Sonya use?

3. For the past 2 nights, Kelsey read $\frac{5}{12}$ of her novel each night. Did Kelsey read the entire novel during those 2 nights?

LEARN

Fraction and Whole Number Products (C)

Model Fraction Multiplication

You can use a grid to determine a fraction of a whole number.

PROBLEM Bryce has 9 eggs. He makes an omelet with $\frac{2}{3}$ of the eggs. How many eggs does he use?

SOLUTION 1 Make a grid that shows 9 equal parts. Then divide the grid into 3 equal sections (thirds). Shade $\frac{2}{3}$ of the grid: $\frac{2}{3}$ of 9 is 6.

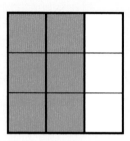

SOLUTION 2 $\frac{2}{3} \times 9 = \frac{2 \times 9}{3} = \frac{18}{3} = 6$

ANSWER Bryce uses 6 eggs to make his omelet.

Solve.

1. Chuck has $72. He buys a book with $\frac{1}{8}$ of his money. How much does he spend on the book?

2. The coaches reported that 20 children were at soccer practice last Saturday. If $\frac{3}{5}$ of the children wore green jerseys, how many children wore green jerseys?

L E A R N

Write a multiplication expression to represent the problem. Then solve.

3. Robinson's basketball team scored 50 points in the first half of a game. Robinson scored $\frac{1}{2}$ of those points. How many points did he score?

4. The food pantry has 60 pounds of flour. Volunteers give out $\frac{5}{6}$ of the flour in a morning. How many pounds of flour do they give out?

5. George's grandma is $\frac{7}{10}$ the age of his great-grandma. His great-grandma is 90 years old. How old is George's grandma?

6. Melanie has 12 cups of soup. She wants to use $\frac{1}{4}$ of it in a recipe. How many cups will she use?

7. There are 88 bookcases in the library's basement. If $\frac{1}{8}$ of the bookcases hold softcover books, how many bookcases that hold softcover books are in the basement?

LEARN

Fraction and Whole Number Products (D)

Products of Fractions and Whole Numbers

Worked Examples

You can simplify factors before you multiply a fraction by a whole number.

PROBLEM 1 Rosa recorded 48 minutes of music. She listens to $\frac{3}{4}$ of the music. For how many minutes does Rosa listen to music?

SOLUTION Write a multiplication expression to model the problem. The fraction factor, $\frac{3}{4}$, is already in simplest form.

$$\frac{3}{4} \times 48 = \frac{3 \times 48}{4} = \frac{144}{4} = 36$$

ANSWER Rosa listens to 36 minutes of music.

PROBLEM 2 Marcus collected 90 state quarters. Exactly $\frac{6}{9}$ of them are California quarters. How many California quarters does Marcus have?

SOLUTION 1 Make a grid to model the problem. You can find $\frac{6}{9}$ of 90 or $\frac{2}{3}$ of 90. In each grid, 60 squares are shaded. The products are equivalent.

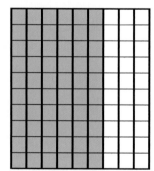 $\frac{6}{9} \times 90 = 60$

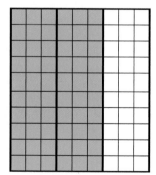 $\frac{2}{3} \times 90 = 60$

SOLUTION 2

1 Write a multiplication expression to model the problem. $\frac{6}{9} \times 90$

2 Simplify the fraction factor. $\frac{6}{9} = \frac{6 \div 3}{9 \div 3} = \frac{2}{3}$

3 Multiply using the simplified factor. $\frac{6}{9} \times 90 = \frac{2}{3} \times 90 = \frac{2 \times 90}{3} = \frac{180}{3} = 60$

ANSWER Marcus has 60 California quarters.

Solve.

1. Jenna has an animal pen with 96 feet of fence around it. A swinging gate is $\frac{1}{8}$ as long as the total fence. How many feet long is the gate?

2. Danny is $\frac{8}{10}$ as tall as his older sister. His sister is 60 inches tall. How tall is Danny?

3. There are 56 ounces of soup left in the chowder pot. The pot will be empty if each person has $\frac{1}{8}$ of the soup. How much soup will each person get?

4. Rosa practices piano for 63 minutes. She spends $\frac{1}{3}$ of the time practicing scales. For how many minutes does Rosa practice scales?

5. Jeffrey read $\frac{4}{12}$ of his book. If his book has 90 pages, how many pages did Jeffrey read?

Challenge Question

Solve.

6. Doug spends $\frac{7}{8}$ of his $64, and Kendra spends $\frac{10}{12}$ of her $78. Who has more money left? How much more?

LEARN

Core Focus
Apply Fraction Operations

Use Fraction Operations

Solve.

1. A pear tree is 590 centimeters tall. $\left(1 \text{ cm} = \frac{1}{100} \text{ m}\right)$

   (a) Determine the height of the pear tree in meters. Write an expression that uses fraction multiplication.

   (b) Use your expression from Part (a) to determine the height of the pear tree in meters. Express your answer as a mixed number.

   (c) The pear tree grows another $\frac{1}{10}$ meter. How many meters tall is the pear tree now? Express your answer in simplest form.

2. The line plot displays the weights of each Granny Smith apple in a grocery bin. The weights were measured to the nearest eighth of a pound.

Apple Weights

```
                        X
              X     X   X
              X     X   X   X
              X     X   X   X
        X     X     X   X   X
    <---+---+---+---+---+---+---+---+---+--->
        0   1/8  1/4  3/8 1/2  5/8 3/4  7/8  1
```

Weight (lb)

   (a) Michael buys all the apples that weigh $\frac{1}{2}$ lb. What is the total weight of the apples that Michael bought? Show your work.

   (b) The apples cost $2 per pound. How much did Michael pay for his apples?

   (c) How many of the apples in the bin weighed more than $\frac{1}{2}$ pound?

3. Evie, her mother, and her father shared a large pizza for dinner. Evie ate $\frac{3}{12}$ of the pizza, her mother ate $\frac{3}{12}$ of the pizza, and her father ate $\frac{4}{12}$ of the pizza. Is there enough pizza left over for Evie to have the same amount for lunch tomorrow as she did for dinner? Explain your reasoning.

TRY IT

Think Like a Mathematician Self-Check

4. State the actions and thinking you used during this lesson as a math learner.

Math Thinking and Actions
I made sense of problems by • Explaining to myself what a problem means and what it asks for • Using drawings or diagrams to represent a problem I was solving
I explained my math thinking clearly.
I tried out new ways to check if an answer is reasonable.
Other

TRY IT

Decimal Numbers

Decimal Expanded Form

You can write a decimal number in expanded form to show the value of each digit.

PROBLEM 1 Write 0.36 in expanded form.

SOLUTION Use a place-value chart to find the value of each digit.

Thousands			Hundreds	Tens	Ones	Tenths	Hundredths
Hundred Thousands	Ten Thousands	Thousands					
					0	3	6

ANSWER 3 tenths + 6 hundredths or 0.3 + 0.06

PROBLEM 2 Write 1,907.09 in expanded form.

SOLUTION Use a place-value chart to find the value of each digit.

Thousands			Hundreds	Tens	Ones	Tenths	Hundredths
Hundred Thousands	Ten Thousands	Thousands					
		1	9	0	7	0	9

ANSWER 1 thousand + 9 hundreds + 7 ones + 9 hundredths or 1,000 + 900 + 7 + 0.09

LEARN

Write the decimal number in expanded form two different ways:

(a) with words and numbers
(b) with numbers only

1. 1.2

2. 2.03

3. 5.47

4. 0.6

5. 0.08

6. 31.15

7. 406.06

8. 7,777.7

LEARN

Decimal and Fraction Equivalents (A)

Decimals and Fractions

You can write equivalent decimal numbers for fractions expressed in tenths and hundredths. You can also write equivalent fractions for decimal numbers expressed in tenths and hundredths.

PROBLEM Rosa listened to 0.3 of a song. Write one equivalent decimal number and two equivalent fractions that tell how much of the song Rosa heard.

SOLUTION

1 Draw four number lines from 0 to 1 that have tick marks at each tenth. Label the endpoints and the halfway point on each number line. Locate and label 0.3 on the first number line.

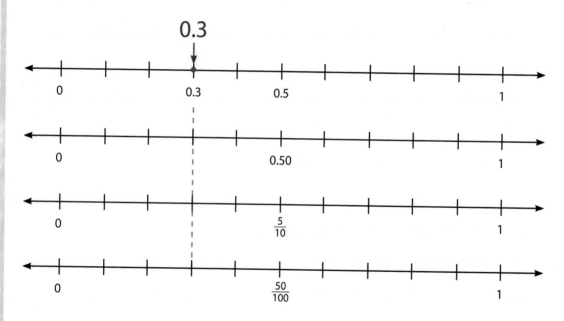

2 Draw a vertical line to locate one point on the decimal number line and one point on each of the fraction number lines that are lined up under 0.3. Then start at 0 and count by tenths or hundredths until you reach the vertical line at points 0.30, $\frac{3}{10}$, and $\frac{30}{100}$.

ANSWER The decimal number 0.30 and the fractions $\frac{3}{10}$ and $\frac{30}{100}$ are equivalent to 0.3.

Solve.

1. Johnny has many pets, and $\frac{7}{10}$ of his pets are dogs. Write two equivalent decimal numbers and one equivalent fraction that tell what fraction many of Johnny's pets are dogs.

2. A paintbrush is 0.4 inches wide. Write two equivalent fractions and one equivalent decimal number that tell the width of the paintbrush.

3. A block of cheese weighs $\frac{6}{10}$ pound. Write two decimal numbers that tell the weight of the cheese.

Choose the answer.

4. Which fraction is equivalent to 0.8?

   A. $\frac{0.8}{10}$ B. $\frac{8}{10}$ C. $\frac{0.8}{100}$ D. $\frac{8}{100}$

5. Which decimal number is equivalent to $\frac{42}{100}$?

   A. 0.42   B. 4.2   C. 42.0   D. 4.20

6. Which **two** decimal numbers are equivalent to $\frac{9}{10}$?

   A. 9.0   B. 0.9   C. 0.90   D. 90.0

LEARN

Decimal and Fraction Equivalents (A)

Fractions and Decimals — Same Value

Solve.

1. Bess walked $\frac{1}{10}$ mile to see her friend. Write three equivalent ways to tell how far Bess walked.

2. Gordon drove 0.8 of the distance from his house to the park. Write three equivalent ways to tell how much of the distance Gordon drove.

Choose the answer.

3. Which fraction is equivalent to 0.4?

   A. $\frac{0.4}{10}$

   B. $\frac{4}{10}$

   C. $\frac{0.4}{100}$

   D. $\frac{4}{100}$

4. Which **two** fractions are equivalent to 0.8?

   A. $\frac{0.8}{10}$

   B. $\frac{0.80}{100}$

   C. $\frac{8}{10}$

   D. $\frac{80}{100}$

5. Which decimal number is equivalent to $\frac{17}{100}$?

   A. 0.17

   B. 1.7

   C. 17.0

   D. 17.00

6. Which **two** decimal numbers are equivalent to $\frac{2}{10}$?

   A. 2.0

   B. 0.2

   C. 20.0

   D. 0.20

7. Which fraction is equivalent to 0.6?

   A. $\frac{0.6}{10}$

   B. $\frac{0.6}{100}$

   C. $\frac{6}{10}$

   D. $\frac{6}{100}$

8. Which decimal number is equivalent to $\frac{5}{10}$?

   A. 0.05

   B. 0.5

   C. 5.0

   D. 50.0

9. Which decimal number is equivalent to $\frac{23}{100}$?

   A. 0.0023

   B. 0.023

   C. 0.23

   D. 2.3

10. Which decimal number is equivalent to $\frac{33}{100}$?

    A. 0.33

    B. 3.3

    C. 33.0

    D. 330.0

11. Which **two** fractions are equivalent to 0.3?

    A. $\frac{0.3}{10}$

    B. $\frac{3}{10}$

    C. $\frac{3}{100}$

    D. $\frac{30}{100}$

12. Which **two** fractions are equivalent to 0.5?

    A. $\frac{5}{10}$

    B. $\frac{0.5}{10}$

    C. $\frac{5}{100}$

    D. $\frac{50}{100}$

13. Which **two** decimal numbers are equivalent to $\frac{7}{10}$?

    A. 0.7

    B. 0.70

    C. 7.0

    D. 70.0

14. Which decimal number is equivalent to $\frac{6}{100}$?

    A. 6.0

    B. 0.06

    C. 0.6

    D. 60.0

TRY IT

Decimal and Fraction Equivalents (B)

Find Equivalent Fractions and Decimals

> ### Worked Examples

You can identify equivalent fractions and decimal numbers more than one way. You can use what you know about money, and you can use number lines.

PROBLEM Write a fraction and a decimal that are equivalent to 6.50.

SOLUTION 1

1 Use what you know about the value of a quarter to make a chart. There are 4 quarters in 1 dollar, so 1 quarter is one-fourth of a dollar, or $\frac{1}{4}$ of a dollar, or 0.25 of a dollar. Refer to the chart for equivalent values.

Number of quarters	Decimal equivalent	Fraction equivalent
1 quarter	0.25	$\frac{1}{4}$
2 quarters	$0.50 = 0.5$	$\frac{2}{4} = \frac{1}{2}$
3 quarters	0.75	$\frac{3}{4}$
4 quarters	1.00	$\frac{4}{4}$

2 $6.50 = 6.5 = 6\frac{2}{4} = 6\frac{1}{2}$

SOLUTION 2

1 Draw number lines. Find a fraction and a decimal number that are located in the same position as 6.50.

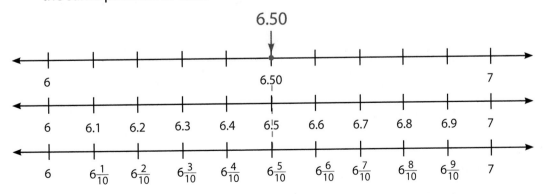

2 Draw a vertical line to locate a point on the second number line and a point on the third number line exactly under 6.50. Both 6.5 and $6\frac{5}{10}$ are lined up under 6.50, so $6.50 = 6.5 = 6\frac{5}{10} = 6\frac{1}{2}$.

ANSWER Both 6.5 and $6\frac{1}{2}$ are equivalent to 6.50.

Solve.

1. Write a fraction and a decimal number that are equivalent to $4\frac{1}{2}$.

2. Write a fraction and a decimal number that are equivalent to $9\frac{1}{4}$.

Choose the answer.

3. Which fraction is equivalent to 0.25?

    A. $\frac{1}{4}$ B. $\frac{2}{5}$ C. $\frac{3}{4}$ D. $\frac{1}{10}$

4. Which fraction is equivalent to 4.75?

    A. $4\frac{1}{4}$ B. $3\frac{3}{4}$ C. $4\frac{7}{5}$ D. $4\frac{3}{4}$

5. Which decimal number is equivalent to $2\frac{1}{2}$?

    A. 2.1   B. 1.5   C. 2.5   D. 2.12

6. Which decimal number is equivalent to $8\frac{3}{4}$?

    A. 8.34   B. 8.25   C. 7.34   D. 8.75

7. Which **two** decimal numbers are equivalent to $3\frac{1}{2}$?

    A. 3.12   B. 3.5   C. 3.2   D. 3.50

8. Which **two** decimal numbers are equivalent to $\frac{1}{2}$?

    A. 1.2   B. 0.12   C. 0.5   D. 0.50

9. Which **two** fractions are equivalent to 4.75?

    A. $4\frac{5}{7}$ B. $4\frac{3}{4}$ C. $4\frac{9}{12}$ D. $4\frac{10}{12}$

10. Which **two** fractions are equivalent to 1.5?

    A. $1\frac{2}{4}$ B. $1\frac{3}{4}$ C. $1\frac{1}{5}$ D. $1\frac{3}{6}$

Decimal and Fraction Equivalents (C)

Different Ways to Show the Same Thing

Write the fraction as a decimal.

1. $\frac{4}{10}$

2. $\frac{9}{100}$

3. $\frac{4}{5}$

Write the decimal as a fraction.

4. 0.2

5. 0.7

6. 0.05

Solve.

7. Write 36 hundredths as a fraction and a decimal.

8. Julia drank $\frac{9}{10}$ cup of juice and 0.9 cup of water.

   Did Julia drink more water, more juice, or the same amounts of water and juice? Explain your answer.

Choose the answer.

9. Mike shaded $\frac{7}{10}$ of this rectangle.

   Which decimal equals $\frac{7}{10}$?

   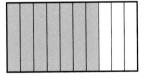

   A. 0.07　　　B. 0.7　　　C. 7.0　　　D. 7.10

10. Petros shaded $\frac{1}{2}$ of this rectangle.

    Which decimal equals $\frac{1}{2}$?

    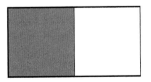

    A. 0.5　　　B. 0.21　　　C. 5.0　　　D. 0.2

TRY IT

Choose the answer.

11. Remi shaded 0.6 of this rectangle. Which fraction equals 0.6?

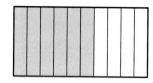

   A. $\frac{1}{6}$ B. $\frac{3}{5}$ C. $\frac{6}{1}$ D. $\frac{5}{3}$

12. Which decimal is equal to $\frac{1}{10}$?

   A. 0.01 B. 0.10 C. 1.0 D. 1.1

13. Which decimal is equal to $\frac{5}{10}$?

   A. 0.5 B. 0.51 C. 5.0 D. 5.1

14. Which fraction is equal to 0.4?

   A. $\frac{1}{4}$ B. $\frac{0}{4}$ C. $\frac{2}{5}$ D. $\frac{4}{100}$

15. Which fraction is equal to 0.3?

   A. $\frac{3}{100}$ B. $\frac{1}{30}$ C. $\frac{3}{10}$ D. $\frac{1}{3}$

16. Which fraction is equal to 0.75?

   A. $\frac{75}{1}$ B. $\frac{3}{4}$ C. $\frac{1}{75}$ D. $\frac{3}{100}$

17. Which fraction is equal to 0.5?

   A. $\frac{1}{2}$ B. $\frac{5}{100}$ C. $\frac{10}{5}$ D. $\frac{2}{10}$

TRY IT

Decimal and Fraction Equivalents (D)

Same Amount in Fraction and Decimal

Write the number as a fraction.

1. 0.7

2. 0.25

3. 0.02

Write the number as a decimal.

4. $\frac{2}{5}$

5. $\frac{1}{2}$

6. $\frac{3}{4}$

Write the number as a decimal in tenths and hundredths. Write the equivalent fractions with denominators of tenths and hundredths.

7. $\frac{1}{2}$

8. $\frac{1}{5}$

9. $\frac{4}{5}$

Solve.

10. Draw a number line that shows $\frac{2}{4}$.

Write a fraction and a decimal that equal $\frac{2}{4}$.

11. Write 3 tenths as a fraction and as a decimal. Use a number line to show why they represent the same quantity.

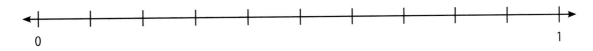

12. Johnny and Winnie are weaving identical placemats. Johnny has completed 0.4 of his placemat and Winnie has completed $\frac{2}{5}$ of her placemat. Who has the least amount left to weave? Explain.

TRY IT

Choose the answer.

13. Which decimal is equal to $\frac{7}{10}$?

    A. 0.07   B. 0.071   C. 0.7   D. 0.71

14. Which decimal is equal to $\frac{3}{5}$?

    A. 0.6   B. 6.0   C. 0.35   D. 3.5

15. Which fraction is equal to 0.25?

    A. $\frac{25}{10}$ B. $\frac{1}{25}$ C. $\frac{10}{25}$ D. $\frac{25}{100}$

16. Which fraction is equal to 0.6?

    A. $\frac{6}{1}$ B. $\frac{5}{3}$ C. $\frac{3}{5}$ D. $\frac{1}{6}$

17. Which decimal is equal to $\frac{4}{5}$?

    A. 4.0, because this is the same as $\frac{4}{10}$, which simplifies to $\frac{4}{5}$

    B. 8.0, because this is the same as $\frac{8}{10}$, which simplifies to $\frac{4}{5}$

    C. 0.8, because this is the same as $\frac{8}{10}$, which simplifies to $\frac{4}{5}$

    D. 0.4, because this is the same as $\frac{4}{10}$, which simplifies to $\frac{4}{5}$

TRY IT

Relate Decimal Numbers to Fractions

Decimal Numbers to Fractions

Write an equivalent fraction for the decimal number.

1. 0.75

2. 0.6

3. 0.2

4. 0.50

Solve.

5. Sketch a number line like the one shown. Put a dot on it to show the fraction $\frac{1}{2}$.

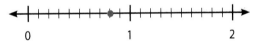

Choose the answer.

6. Which fraction is shown on this number line?

A. $1\frac{2}{10}$

B. $1\frac{1}{5}$

C. $1\frac{1}{4}$

D. $1\frac{3}{4}$

7. Which decimal number is shown on this number line?

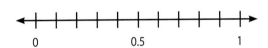

A. 0.45

B. 0.8

C. 0.9

D. 0.5

8. Which shows a decimal equivalent to $2\frac{7}{10}$ on the number line?

A.

B.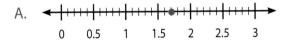

C.

D.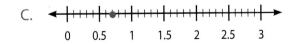

9. Which shows a fraction equivalent to 2.75 on the number line?

A.

B.

C.

D.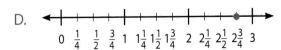

TRY IT

Compare Decimals

Greater or Less?

Worked Examples

You can use place value to compare decimal numbers.

PROBLEM Use > and < to write two statements to compare 320.3 and 320.03.

SOLUTION

1 Write numbers with the same number of decimal places, if needed.

320.30 and 320.03

2 Start at the far left place-value position. Find the first pair of digits that differ. Compare them.

3 tenths > 0 tenths

3 Write two comparison statements using the numbers from the original problem.

320.3 > 320.03
320.03 < 320.3

ANSWER 320.3 > 320.03, 320.03 < 320.3

Use > and < to write **two** statements to compare the numbers.

1. 1,323.99 and 1,324.01

2. 203.02 and 20.32

3. 78.45 and 78.48

Use <, >, or = to compare the numbers.

4. 106.06 __?__ 106.60

5. 34.3 __?__ 34.30

6. 3,482.3 __?__ 3,482.08

Solve.

7. Monya has two large dogs. Sandy weighs 50.2 kilograms and Mocca weighs 50.19 kilograms. Which dog weighs less, or do they weigh the same?

8. Caryn threw a ball 34.62 meters. George threw a ball 34.7 meters. Who threw the ball farther, or did they throw the same distance?

9. Molly swam 32.9 laps. Tom swam 32.90 laps. Who swam farther, or did they swim the same distance?

LEARN

Solve.

1. On Monday, 0.25 inches of rain fell. On Tuesday, 0.4 inches of rain fell.

   (a) Express each amount of rainfall as a fraction.

   (b) Risa says that more rain fell Monday because 25 is greater than 4. Is Risa correct? Explain why or why not.

2. Jonah walked 2 kilometers on a treadmill. Rob walked 1.75 kilometers on a treadmill.

   (a) Who walked a greater distance? Explain.

   (b) Jonah and Rob each listened to music for 0.5 of the distance they walked. Did they listen to music for the same number of kilometers? Explain.

3. Olympic sprinter Usain Bolt ran a 100-meter race in 10.06 seconds.

   (a) Between what two whole numbers is 10.06 on a number line?

   (b) Another runner completed the same race in 10.1 seconds. Was that runner's time faster or slower than Bolt's? Explain.

4. A penny is 1 hundredth of a dollar. A dime is 1 tenth of a dollar.

   (a) A nickel is equal to 5 pennies. Express the value of a nickel as both a fraction of a dollar and a decimal. Explain your reasoning.

   (b) Alden has 1 dime. Sam has 2 nickels. Compare the amounts of money Alden and Sam have. Show your work or explain your reasoning.

TRY IT

5. State the actions and thinking you used during this lesson as a math learner.

Math Thinking and Actions
I made sense of problems by   • Explaining to myself what a problem means and what it asks for   • Using drawings or diagrams to represent a problem I was solving
I explained my math thinking clearly.
I tried out new ways to check if an answer is reasonable.
Other

TRY IT

Analyze Story Problems (B)

Use a Problem-Solving Plan

Worked Examples

You can use a 4-step problem-solving plan to solve a story problem. When you solve a multistep problem, you can break it into simpler parts.

PROBLEM Hannah is at a choir concert. The choir sings 5 songs that are each about 3 minutes long. The choir stands in two different sections with 6 rows in each section. In the first section, there are 5 members in each row. In the second section, there are 6 members in each row. Three-fifths of the choir members are girls. The rest are boys. How many members are there in the choir?

SOLUTION

UNDERSTAND THE PROBLEM You need to find out how many members there are in the choir. First you need to find out how many members stand in each of the sections.

You do **not** need to know how many songs the choir sings, how long each song is, or how many choir members are girls or boys.

DEVISE A PLAN

1 Find the number of choir members that stand in the first section.

2 Find the number of choir members that stand in the second section.

3 Write an equation to find the total number of choir members that stand in both sections. Then solve.

CARRY OUT THE PLAN

1 There are 6 rows in the first section. Five choir members stand in each row. Multiply 6 rows by 5 choir members per row.
$6 \times 5 = 30$; 30 choir members

2 There are 6 rows in the second section. Six choir members stand in each row. Multiply 6 rows by 6 choir members per row.
$6 \times 6 = 36$; 36 choir members

3 $30 + 36 = t$
30 members + 36 members = 66 members

LEARN

LOOK BACK Make sure you've answered the question that was asked. You can use inverse operations to check your work.

- Does 6 rows × 5 members = 30 members?
  Yes, because 30 ÷ 5 = 6.
- Does 6 rows × 6 members = 36 members?
  Yes, because 36 ÷ 6 = 6.
- Does 30 members + 36 members = 66 members?
  Yes, because 66 − 36 = 30.

ANSWER There are 66 members in the choir.

Solve. Use the problem-solving plan. Show how you looked back to check your answer.

1. Stephen is planning a party for 13 people. Everyone will have 30 minutes to eat dinner. He will serve pizza. One pizza feeds 6 people. During the party, he wants to play 3 games. Two of the games will take 15 minutes each. One game will take 20 minutes. Stephen will give each guest 2 party favors. He will start the party activities 10 minutes after the party starts to give all his guests a chance to arrive. Stephen wants his party to end at 8:00 p.m.

   At what time should Stephen's party start?

2. Yolanda, Jerry, and Sarah collect trading cards. A card box holds 35 cards. A card album holds 40 cards. Yolanda has 45 cards. Jerry has an album full of cards. Sarah has two full boxes of cards.

   How many more cards would Yolanda have to get to have the same number of cards as Sarah?

L E A R N

Analyze Story Problems (B)

Solve Problems

Explain the steps you can use to solve the problem.

1. The baker used 52 cups of white flour, 13 cups of wheat flour, and 7 cups of sugar every day. How much flour did the baker use in 5 days?

Identify the information that is necessary to solve the problem.

2. Margaret curls up on the sofa and reads for 30 minutes and then plays outside for 45 minutes on Saturday and 45 minutes on Sunday. For how many minutes does Margaret play outside on the weekend?

Choose the plan that solves the problem.

3. Sarah is assembling 1 bag for each of 7 participants in a competition. She puts 2 shirts and 12 pins in each bag. In each bag she also puts 3 instruction packets. How many shirts and pins did Sarah put in the bags altogether?

   A. Add the number of shirts in each bag to 7. Add the number of pins in each bag to 7. Then add those sums.

   B. Add the number of shirts in each bag to the number of pins in each bag. Multiply that sum by 7.

   C. Multiply the number of shirts in each bag by 7. Multiply the number of pins in each bag by 3. Then add those products.

4. Solei washed 3 loads of laundry on the weekend and 2 loads of laundry during the week. Each load takes 35 minutes to wash and uses 5 gallons of water per load. How much water did Solei use to do his laundry?

   A. **Step 1:** Add $3 + 2$.
      Step 2: Multiply the sum by 35.

   B. **Step 1:** Add $3 + 2$.
      Step 2: Multiply the sum by 5.

   C. **Step 1:** Multiply 3×5.
      Step 2: Add 35 to the product.

   D. **Step 1:** Multiply 2×35.
      Step 2: Add 5 to the product.

TRY IT

Multistep Problems

Solve Multistep Problems

Worked Examples

To solve a multistep problem, you can break the problem into simpler parts.

PROBLEM Mr. Zimmer is building steps to his porch. He needs 4 boards that are each 12 feet long. He needs 6 boards that are each 18 feet long. How many feet of board does Mr. Zimmer need in all?

SOLUTION

UNDERSTAND THE PROBLEM You need to find out how many total feet of board Mr. Zimmer needs to build the steps. You'll need to find how many feet of 12-foot-long boards he needs and how many feet of 18-foot-long boards he needs.

DEVISE A PLAN Break this multistep problem into simpler parts.

1 Find how many feet of 12-foot-long boards he needs.

2 Find how many feet of 18-foot-long boards he needs.

3 Write an equation to find the total number of feet of board Mr. Zimmer needs. Then solve.

CARRY OUT THE PLAN

1 There are 4 boards. Each board is 12 feet long.
Multiply 4 boards by 12 feet per board.
$4 \times 12 = 48$

2 There are 6 boards. Each board is 18 feet long.
Multiply 6 boards by 18 feet per board.
$6 \times 18 = 108$

3 $48 + 108 = t$
$156 = t$

LOOK BACK Make sure you've answered the question that was asked. Estimate the answer: about 150 feet (50 feet + 100 feet = 150 feet). Since 156 feet is close to the estimate of 150 feet, the answer makes sense.

ANSWER Mr. Zimmer needs 156 feet of board.

LEARN

Solve.

1. Katie is having a party. She wants to tape paper streamers from the ceiling. Each red streamer is 6 feet long and each yellow streamer is 7 feet long. If Katie hangs 10 red streamers and 7 yellow streamers, how many feet of paper streamers will she use altogether?

    (a) What are the simpler parts of the problem?

    (b) What is the answer to the problem?

2. Josh needs to buy 4 cans of paint. Al's Paint and Go sells paint for $12 a can. Bob's Paint Shop sells paint for $22 for 2 cans. Mazzeo's Paint and Stuff sells paint for $52 for 4 cans. At which store is the paint the least expensive? How much will Josh save by buying the paint at that store rather than either of the other two stores?

    (a) What are the simpler parts of the problem?

    (b) What is the answer to the problem?

3. Tyson and Jonathan go to the Snack Shack for lunch. Tyson buys a special, a chef salad, and a large drink. Jonathan buys two specials. Who spends more? How much more?

    (a) What are the simpler parts of the problem?

    (b) What is the answer to the problem?

Menu	
Chef Salad	$5
Hamburger	$5
Hot Dog	$4
Chicken Sandwich	$5

Drink
   medium
   large
	$1
	$2

Chips	$1
Special 1 meal + medium drink + chips	$6

LEARN

Estimate to Predict and Verify (A)

Estimate with Mental Math

Worked Examples

You can estimate to solve a story problem that does not require an exact answer.

PROBLEM Last week a 747 jet airliner made 18 flights with no empty seats. If each flight carried 222 passengers, about how many passengers did the airliner carry last week?

SOLUTION

UNDERSTAND THE PROBLEM The question is, "About how many passengers did the airliner carry last week?" So the answer should be an estimate, not an exact solution.

DEVISE A PLAN You need to break the problem into three parts. Use friendly numbers to round. Use mental math to solve.

1 Round the number of flights to the nearest ten.

2 Round the number of passengers per flight to the nearest hundred.

3 Write an equation to multiply the estimated number of flights by the estimated number of passengers. Then solve.

CARRY OUT THE PLAN

1 Round 18 flights to 20 flights.

2 Round 222 passengers to 200 passengers.

3 $20 \times 200 = p$
$20 \times 200 = 4,000$; The airliner carried about 4,000 passengers last week.

LOOK BACK Reread the problem to be sure you answered the question. Use a number line or place-value chart to be sure you rounded correctly. Then use the inverse operation of division to check your calculation. Does $4,000 \div 20 = 200$? Yes.

ANSWER The airliner carried about 4,000 passengers last week.

LEARN

Write an equation you can use to estimate the answer. Then solve.

1. Last week a 747 jet airliner made 9 flights with no empty seats. If 1,998 passengers flew on the jet last week, about how many passengers were on each flight?

2. A flower shop has 4,867 carnations to tie in bunches with 7 carnations in each bunch. About how many bunches of carnations will the flower shop have?

3. The best tickets to one New York City play cost $288 each. If 42 people buy those tickets, about how much money will the box office collect for the best tickets?

Identify the two steps you need to solve the problem. Then estimate to complete each step.

4. During the first week of the county fair, 19,793 people attended the fair. During the second week of the fair, 13,123 attended. Last year 40,000 people attended during the two weeks. About how many more people attended last year than this year?

5. During the first two weeks of the county fair, 23,028 people used student passes and 9,888 people used regular tickets. Student tickets cost $4 each, and regular tickets cost $5 each. About how much more money was spent on student tickets than regular tickets?

LEARN

Estimate to Predict and Verify (A)

Estimation with Story Problems

Solve.

1. The population of a small city is 45,925. There are about 4 people in each family in the city. Suppose the population decreases by 1,099 people.

   About how many families would there be in the city after the decrease?

Choose the answer.

2. A stamp collector has 1,176 stamps from 6 different countries. He has an equal number of stamps from each country. How many stamps does the stamp collector have from each country?

   Which expression will give the most accurate estimate?

   A. $1,800 \div 6$

   B. $1,200 \div 6$

   C. $1,200 \div 5$

   D. $1,299 \times 6$

3. A bird-watching club has an outing once a year. The members counted 469 birds the first year, 613 birds the second year, and 525 birds the third year. A student answered that the club saw 1,607 birds in the 3 years of bird-watching outings.

   Which statement is true about this student's answer?

   A. The answer should be about 1,600. The student's answer is correct.

   B. The answer should be about 1,500. The student's answer is not correct.

   C. The answer should be about 15,000. The student's answer is not correct.

   D. The answer should be about 16,000. The student's answer is not correct.

4. A theater group sold tickets for 29 days before the performance. If the group sold 87 tickets each day, about how many tickets did the members sell in the 29 days?

   Which expression will give the most accurate estimate?

   A. $90 + 30$

   B. 80×30

   C. $90 \div 30$

   D. 90×30

Estimate to Predict and Verify (B)

Analyze and Solve Story Problems

You can estimate the answer to a story problem. Then you can solve the problem and compare your exact answer to your estimate. If the two values are close, then your answer is reasonable.

PROBLEM An office building with 8 floors has 39 lamps on each floor. Each lamp holds 1 light bulb. The building manager is replacing old light bulbs with energy-saving bulbs. So far, she has replaced 53 bulbs. How many bulbs does she still need to replace?

SOLUTION

UNDERSTAND THE PROBLEM You need to find out how many light bulbs the building manager still needs to replace after she replaces 53 bulbs. But first you need to find out how many total lamps are in the building.

DEVISE A PLAN You need to break this multistep problem into three parts.

1 Estimate the answer to the story problem.

2 Find the number of lamps, each needing 1 light bulb.

3 Write an equation to subtract 53 from the total number of lamps. Then solve.

CARRY OUT THE PLAN

1 Round 39 to 40. There are about 40 lamps on each floor. There are 8 floors. Use mental math to multiply $40 \times 8 = 320$. So you know there are about 320 lamps in all. Round 53 to 50. About 50 bulbs have been replaced.
$320 - 50 = n$; $320 - 50 = 270$; About 270 light bulbs still need to be replaced.

2 There are 39 lamps on each floor with 1 bulb in each lamp. $39 \times 1 = 39$
There are 8 floors with 39 bulbs to replace on each floor. $8 \times 39 = 312$
There are 312 lamps in the building.

3 $312 - 53 = n$; $312 - 53 = 259$

LEARN

LOOK BACK Compare the exact answer to the estimate. Since an answer of 259 light bulbs is fairly close to the estimate of 270 light bulbs, then the answer is reasonable but should be checked again for accuracy.

ANSWER The building manager still needs to replace 259 light bulbs.

Estimate the answer, and then solve. Use the estimate to explain why the answer is reasonable.

1. How many yards of rope are needed to make eighteen 6-foot jump ropes and thirty-one 9-foot jump ropes? There are 3 feet in 1 yard.

   Estimate?
   Exact answer?
   Explanation?

2. A farmer has 9 cartons of potatoes. Each carton weighs 59 pounds. If all the potatoes are about the same weight and size, how many 3-pound bags of potatoes can the farmer make?

   Estimate?
   Exact answer?
   Explanation?

3. A restaurant has 19 inside tables that can each seat 6 people. It has 11 outside tables that can each seat 4 people. How many people in all can be seated inside and outside the restaurant?

   Estimate?
   Exact answer?
   Explanation?

LEARN

Estimate to Predict and Verify (B)
Solve Problems with Data from Tables

Worked Examples

You can solve story problems with data from tables. You can compare your exact answer to an estimate, or prediction, to be sure your answer is reasonable.

PROBLEM Steve buys 93 bags of doggie treats. He repackages them in 9-ounce portions. How many portions will he have?

Treats	Price
doggie treat 21 oz bag	$3.80

SOLUTION

UNDERSTAND THE PROBLEM The problem is asking how many 9-ounce portions of doggie treats Steve will have.

DEVISE A PLAN Break this multistep problem into three parts. Use the information in the table to solve one or more of the parts.

1 Make a written estimate.

2 Find the number of ounces of doggie treats that Steve has in all.

3 Write an equation to divide the total ounces of doggie treats into 9-ounce portions. Then solve.

CARRY OUT THE PLAN

1 Round 93 to 90. Steve buys about 90 bags of treats.
Round 21 to 20. Each bag holds about 20 ounces of treats.
90×20 ounces $= 1,800$; Steve has about 1,800 ounces of treats in all.
Each portion is 9 ounces. Mentally divide $1,800 \div 9 = 200$.
Estimate: Steve has about 200 portions.

2 Each bag has 21 ounces of treats.
93×21 ounces $= 1,953$ ounces

3 $1,953 \div 9 = b$; $1,953 \div 9 = 217$; Exact answer: two hundred seventeen 9-ounce bags

LOOK BACK Compare the estimate to the exact answer. The exact answer of 217 bags is close to the estimate of 200 bags, so it is a reasonable answer.

ANSWER Steve will have 217 bags of doggie treats.

LEARN

Use the tables to solve. First write the estimate. Then write the exact answer.

Dog gates	Sale price
77-inch flexible gate	$115
24-inch gate extension	$35

Collars	Plain	With name
small	$4	$17
medium	$6	$18
large	$7	$20

1. Mrs. Garcia buys 2 flexible gates and 1 extension on sale. How much does she spend?

   Estimate?
   Exact answer?

2. An animal shelter has a discount coupon for $193 off a large purchase at the dog supply store. The shelter buys 113 medium dog collars with names and uses the discount coupon. What will the final price be?

   Estimate?
   Exact answer?

3. Emma bought a flexible gate for a room that is 8 feet wide. The gate is too short for her space. How many inches short is it? (12 inches = 1 foot)

   Estimate?
   Exact answer?

L E A R N

Represent and Explain Story Problems

More Than One Strategy to Solve

You can use different strategies to solve a story problem. You can decide which strategy you want to use.

PROBLEM Johnny saw some animals at a pet store. He saw 4 cats. He saw 3 times as many dogs as cats. He saw 5 fewer hamsters than dogs. How many animals did Johnny see at the pet store?

SOLUTION 1

UNDERSTAND THE PROBLEM You need to find out how many cats Johnny saw, how many dogs he saw, and how many hamsters he saw at the pet store. Then you need to find out how many animals he saw in all.

DEVISE A PLAN You can draw a diagram. Use circles to show the different types of animals. Let C stand for cat, D for dog, and H for hamster.

- Johnny saw 4 cats. Draw 4 circles and write C in each circle.
- He saw 3 times as many dogs as cats. Draw 3 groups of 4 circles and write D in each circle.
- He saw 5 fewer hamsters than dogs. Count the number of D circles and draw 5 fewer circles. Write H in each circle.

CARRY OUT THE PLAN Use the diagram. Count the total number of circles. There are 23 circles, so Johnny saw 23 animals at the pet store.

C = cat   D = dog   H = hamster

LOOK BACK Be sure you answered the question. Reread the problem to be sure you drew the diagram correctly. Count the circles again.

LEARN

SOLUTION 2

UNDERSTAND THE PROBLEM See Solution 1.

DEVISE A PLAN Break this multistep problem into steps.

1 Remember that Johnny saw 4 cats.

2 Find the number of dogs Johnny saw.

3 Find the number of hamsters Johnny saw.

4 Write an equation to find the total number of animals Johnny saw.
   Then solve.

CARRY OUT THE PLAN

1 Johnny saw 4 cats.

2 He saw 3 times the number of dogs as cats. $3 \times 4 = d$; $3 \times 4 = 12$; 12 dogs

3 He saw 5 fewer hamsters than dogs. $12 - 5 = h$; $12 - 5 = 7$; 7 hamsters

4 $4 + 12 + 7 = a$; $4 + 12 + 7 = 23$; 23 animals

LOOK BACK Be sure you answered the question. Reread the problem step-by-step to be sure you computed each part correctly.

ANSWER Johnny saw 23 animals at the pet store.

Explain how to solve the story problem two different ways. Then solve.

1. Kerry invited 16 people to a party. Six people can sit at a long dining-room table. Four people can sit at a square table. What is the fewest number of square tables needed so each guest will have a seat?

2. A recipe calls for 10 grams of sprinkles on each dozen cookies. Lyle wants to decorate 36 cookies. How many grams of sprinkles will Lyle need?

3. A statue of a man is 13 feet tall. The base that it sits on is 5 feet high. It traveled 345 miles to be put in place. How tall is the statue from the bottom of the base to the top of the statue's head?

LEARN

Represent and Explain Story Problems

Same Problem, Different Ways

You can make a table or draw a diagram to solve a story problem.

PROBLEM Sarah has two dogs. Prince eats 2 cans of dog food every 3 days and 1 bag of dry food in 12 days. Bucky eats 2 cans of dog food every 2 days and 2 bags of dry food in 12 days. For how many days can Sarah feed both dogs with 40 cans of dog food and 6 bags of dry food?

SOLUTION 1

UNDERSTAND THE PROBLEM You need to find the number of days Sarah can feed her two dogs with the food that she has.

DEVISE A PLAN Use the make-a-table strategy.

1 Make one table to figure out how many cans Prince eats in 12 days.

2 Make another table to figure out how many cans Bucky eats in 12 days.

3 Compare the total amount of food the dogs eat in 12 days to the total amount of food that Sarah has. Then decide how many days the food will last.

CARRY OUT THE PLAN

1

Prince's Food				
Days	3	6	9	12
Cans	2	4	6	8

Prince eats 8 cans and 1 bag of food in 12 days.

2

Bucky's Food						
Days	2	4	6	8	10	12
Cans	2	4	6	8	10	12

Bucky eats 12 cans and 2 bags of food in 12 days.

3 They eat $8 + 12 = 20$ cans of food and $1 + 2 = 3$ bags of food in 12 days. Since 40 cans of food $= 2 \times 20$ cans and 6 bags of food $= 2 \times 3$ bags, then Sarah will have enough food for 2×12 days $= 24$ days.

LOOK BACK Does 24 days answer the question? Yes, because you need to find for how many days Sarah can feed her dog with 40 cans and 6 bags. That amount is exactly how much food the dogs will eat in 24 days.

SOLUTION 2

UNDERSTAND THE PROBLEM See Solution 1.

DEVISE A PLAN Use the draw-a-diagram strategy.

1 Draw a diagram to find how many cans of food the dogs eat in 12 days.

2 Draw another diagram to find how many bags of food the dogs eat in 12 days.

3 Compare the total amount of food the dogs eat in 12 days to the total amount of food that Sarah has.

CARRY OUT THE PLAN

1 Cans
Days

Prince

Cans
Days

Bucky

Sarah needs $8 + 12 = 20$ cans for 12 days.

2 Bags
Days

Prince

Bags
Days

Bucky

Sarah needs $1 + 2 = 3$ bags for 12 days.

3 The dogs will eat $2 \times 20 = 40$ cans of food and $2 \times 3 = 6$ bags of food in 2×12, or 24 days.

LOOK BACK See Solution 1.

ANSWER With the food she has, Sarah can feed her dogs for 24 days.

Solve the problem two different ways.

1. Alex has $1.40 in his pocket. He has 11 coins in all. He has 3 quarters and a combination of dimes and nickels. How many dimes does Alex have? How many nickels does Alex have?

2. A novelty store has 350 toy figures of popular music stars. Each bin holds 25 figures. How many bins will hold all 350 figures?

3. The Antonini family bought hot dog rolls in packages of 10 and hot dogs in packages of 6. Each adult at the picnic eats 3 hot dogs and 3 hot dog rolls. How many packages of rolls and hot dogs will the family have to buy to feed 20 adults?

LEARN

Represent and Explain Story Problems

Identify Two Strategies

Solve two ways. Explain the strategies.

1. Bryson bought some pencils, pens, and markers at the office supply store. He bought 3 times as many pencils as pens. He bought 5 more markers than pens. He bought 6 pens. How many items did Bryson buy at the office supply store?

Choose the two strategies that can be used to solve the problem.

2. Anna had some flowers. She arranged 18 flowers in each of 8 vases. She had 11 flowers left over. How many flowers did she have to start?

   A. Guess and test. Try starting with 100 flowers. Subtract 21 repeatedly until the difference is less than 21. Count the number of times you subtracted. If you did not subtract 21 eight times and end up with 11 flowers left over, 100 is not right. Adjust the number and repeat.

   B. Write an equation and solve.
   $8 \times 18 + 11 = f$

   C. Draw a picture. Sketch 8 groups of 18, then 11 more, and count them all.

3. Volunteers are setting up benches for an exhibition at a town fair. They will use long benches that can each seat 12 people and short benches that can each seat 5 people. What is the fewest number of short benches that volunteers can set up so that 58 people can have seats?

   A. Draw a picture. Draw 58 dots. Circle as many groups of 12 as you can. Then circle as many groups of 5 as you can from the dots that are not already circled. Count the number of groups of 5.

   B. Work backward. Begin with 58. Subtract 12 repeatedly until the difference is less than 12. Then subtract 5 until the difference is less than 5. Count the number of 5s you subtracted.

   C. Write equations and solve.
   $5 \times 12 = 60$ and $60 - 58 = b$

   D. Explain that 5 times 10 equals 50, so you need 10 short benches.

TRY IT

4. A frozen yogurt shop owner sold vanilla, chocolate, and banana yogurt pops. In 1 hour, the owner sold 1 more banana pop than the number of chocolate pops sold. She sold twice as many vanilla pops as the number of banana pops sold. If the owner sold 7 chocolate pops, how many pops in all did she sell in 1 hour?

A. Work backward. She sold 7 chocolate pops, so multiply 7 by 2 and add 1.

B. Draw a diagram. Draw 7 chocolate pops. Then draw 1 more banana pop than the number of chocolate pops, or 8 banana pops. Then draw 2 times as many vanilla pops as the number of banana pops, or 16 vanilla pops. Count all the yogurt pops to find the total.

C. Use logical thinking. There were 7 chocolate pops. Add 1 to get 8 because 1 more banana pop than the number of chocolate pops was sold. Double the 8 to get 16 because twice as many vanilla as banana pops were sold. Then add $7 + 8 + 16$.

D. Write an equation and solve.
$2 \times 7 + 1 = p$

State Solutions Clearly (A)

Make-a-Table Strategy

Worked Examples

You can make a table to organize the data in a story problem.

PROBLEM Layla recorded the daily high and low temperatures (in degrees Fahrenheit) in her city for five days: Highs: Mon. 81°, Tues. 82°, Wed. 80°, Thurs. 80°, Fri. 79°; Lows: Mon. 63°, Tues. 65°, Wed. 60°, Thurs. 67°, Fri. 62°. On which day was the difference between the high and low temperatures the greatest? Solve and explain how you solved the problem.

SOLUTION

UNDERSTAND THE PROBLEM To see which day of the week had the greatest difference in temperatures, find the difference between the high and low temperatures of each day.

DEVISE A PLAN Use the make-a-table strategy. Arrange the data by days of the week so that the lows can easily be subtracted from the highs. Subtract. Identify the day with the greatest difference. Then explain how you solved the problem.

CARRY OUT THE PLAN

	Mon.	Tues.	Wed.	Thurs.	Fri.
High temp.	81°	82°	80°	80°	79°
Low temp.	63°	65°	60°	67°	62°
Difference	18°	17°	20°	13°	17°

The greatest difference was 20° and occurred on Wednesday.

LOOK BACK Be sure the data on the table matches the data in the problem. Check your subtraction and compare the differences again.

ANSWER The greatest difference occurred on Wednesday. To solve the problem, subtract each day's low temperature from the high temperature, find the greatest difference, and identify the day it occurred.

L E A R N

Complete the table to solve the problem.

1. The city of Twin Lakes has a weeklong town carnival each year. Mr. Buckle recorded the number of adult tickets and child tickets that were sold each day.

Adult tickets:
Mon.	318
Tues.	425
Wed.	376
Thurs.	404
Fri.	418
Sat.	514
Sun.	511

Child tickets:
Mon.	375
Tues.	350
Wed.	480
Thurs.	270
Fri.	500
Sat.	320
Sun.	285

On which day did the carnival sell the most tickets?

How many more tickets were sold on Wednesday than on Tuesday?

Explain how you solved the problem.

	Mon.	Tues.	Wed.	Thur.	Fri.	Sat.	Sun.
Adult tickets	?	?	?	?	?	?	?
Child tickets	?	?	?	?	?	?	?
Total	?	?	?	?	?	?	?

2. Ashley has 1 dime, 5 nickels, and 20 pennies. She found six ways to use some of her coins to show 18¢. Use the table to find the six ways that Ashley can use some of her coins to show 18¢.

Then explain how you solved the problem.

Number of dimes	Number of nickels	Number of pennies	Total value
?	?	?	18¢
?	?	?	18¢
?	?	?	18¢
?	?	?	18¢
?	?	?	18¢
?	?	?	18¢

Read the problem and follow the directions.

3. Write a story problem that uses the data in the table. Then solve the problem and explain how you solved it.

	Art Club	Music Club	Dance Club	Sport Club	Chess Club
Money raised	$675	$715	$682	$764	$520
Expenses	$411	$430	$459	$582	$322
?	?	?	?	?	?

LEARN

Solve and Explain

Explain how to solve the problem, and then solve.

1. Tickets to the zoo cost $15 each for adult tickets and $9 each for child tickets. Mrs. Porter bought 8 tickets. She spent a total of $90. How many of each type of ticket did Mrs. Porter buy?

2. Zeke is saving money to buy a new bike. The bike costs $218. He starts with $42 in his savings account. Each week he deposits $15. How many weeks will it take for Zeke to save enough to buy the bike?

Choose the explanation that best describes how to solve the problem.

3. Elena ran 20 miles every week for 5 weeks. She ran 25 miles the sixth week and 33 miles the seventh week. How far did Elena run in 7 weeks?

   A. **Write an equation.** $20 + 5 + 25 + 6 + 33 + 7 = m$
      Elena ran 96 miles.

   B. **Break up the problem into smaller problems.** Multiply 20 by 5 to get 100 miles in 5 weeks. Add 25 miles and 33 miles to figure out how many miles she ran in the sixth and seventh weeks. Add $100 + 58$ together. Elena ran 158 miles.

   C. **Work backward.** Elena ran 20 miles in 5 weeks. That means she ran 4 miles in 1 week. Add 4 miles to 25 and 33. Elena ran 62 miles.

   D. **Make a table.** Elena ran 33 miles.

Week	1	2	3	4	5	6	7
Miles	20	20	20	20	20	25	33

TRY IT

Choose the explanation that best describes how to solve the problem.

4. The zoo has 32 lizards in an enclosure. Ten of the lizards are yellow, and 6 of the lizards are red. Half of the remaining lizards are green. How many lizards are green?

    A. **Work backward.** Start with the original number of lizards. Divide by 2 because half of the lizards are green, and then subtract 10 and 6.

    B. **Guess and test.** Guess that there are 10 green lizards. Half of 10 is 5. Add 10 and add 6 to get 21. That amount is fewer than the number of lizards in the enclosure, so try again with another number. Guess that there are 40 green lizards. Half of 40 is 20. Add 10 and add 6 to get 36. That amount is more than the number of lizards in the enclosure, so try again with another number. Guess that there are 32 green lizards. Half of 32 is 16. Add 10 and add 6 to get 32.

    C. **Write an equation.** $(32 - 10 - 6) \div 2 = g$

    D. **Make a diagram.** Draw 32 dots to represent the 32 lizards. Cross out 10 of them for the yellow lizards and 6 of them for the red lizards. Take the remaining 16 dots and cross out half of them (8 dots). The number of dots remaining is the number of green lizards in the enclosure.

5. Carl spent 45 minutes on his French project and 1 hour on his math assignment. He talked on the phone for 15 minutes and then drove to his tennis practice. The drive took 20 minutes. His tennis practice started at 5:30 p.m. What time did Carl start his French project?

    A. **Guess and test.** Start at 2:00, and add 45 minutes. The time is now 2:45. Add 1 hour. The time is now 3:45. Add 15 minutes. The time is now 4:00. Add 20 minutes. Carl started his French project at 4:20.

    B. **Write an equation.** $530 - (45 + 1 + 15 + 20) = t$
    Carl started his French project at 4:49.

    C. **Make a diagram.** Draw a clock. First show the minute hand starting at 12. Draw another clock. Add 45 minutes. The minute hand now points to the 9. Draw another clock. Add 1 hour. The minute hand points to the 9. Draw another clock. Add 15 minutes. The minute hand now points to the 12. Draw another clock. Add 20 minutes. The minute hand now points to the 5. Carl started his French project at 25 minutes after the hour.

    D. **Work backward.** Start at 5:30, and subtract 20 minutes; he left for tennis practice at 5:10. Subtract 15 minutes; he started talking on the phone at 4:55. Subtract 1 hour; he started math assignment at 3:55. Subtract 45 minutes. Carl started his French project at 3:10.

TRY IT

Choose the explanation that best describes how to solve the problem.

6. Every month, Susie bought a balloon and a card to give to her grandfather. Each balloon cost $7 and each card cost $2. How much money did Susie spend in 6 months?

A. **Make a table.** Susie spent $54.

Month	1	2	3	4	5	6
Total cost	$9	$18	$27	$36	$45	$54

B. **Draw a picture.** Draw 7 circles and write $7 in each one. Draw 2 circles and write $2 in each one. Add up the amounts in the circles. Susie spent $53.

C. **Use objects to model the problem.** Take 7 blocks and 2 blocks, and put them together to get 9 blocks. Susie spent $9 altogether.

D. **Break the problem into steps.** Multiply the cost of balloons by the cost of the card ($7 × $2). Multiply the cost by the number of months ($14 × $6). Susie spent $84.

7. Rachael rode her bike 15 miles every week for 5 weeks. She rode her bike 18 miles the sixth week and 19 miles the seventh week. How far did Rachael ride her bike in 7 weeks?

A. Add 15 and 5 and 18 and 6 and 19 and 7.

B. Add 15 and 5. Then add 18 and 19. Then add the two sums together.

C. Multiply 15 × 5. Then add 18 and 19 to the product.

D. Divide 15 by 5. Then add 18 and 19 to the quotient.

8. Six boys want to go to the movies and then go for pizza. They have a total of $100. The movie tickets cost $10 each. How much money will the boys have left to buy pizza?

A. Add 6 and 100 and 10.

B. Divide 100 by 6. Then add 10 to the quotient.

C. Multiply 10 × 6. Then subtract the product from 100.

D. Add 10 and 6. Then multiply the sum by 100.

9. This past summer, Alice read 3 books a week for the first 3 weeks and then 2 books a week for the last 3 weeks. How many books did Alice read?

A. Add 3 and 3 and 2 and 3.

B. Add 3 and 2. Multiply the sum by 2.

C. Multiply 3 × 3. Then multiply 2 × 3. Then add the two products.

D. Add 3 and 3. Then divide the sum by 3.

10. The toy factory makes 120 toy cars in a day. Each day 10 of the cars are rejected because they have flaws in the paint. How many flawless cars can the toy factory make in 400 days?

    A. Add 120 and 10 and 400.

    B. Multiply 120 × 10. Subtract the product from 400.

    C. Divide 120 by 10. Add the quotient to 400.

    D. Subtract 10 from 120. Multiply the difference by 400.

11. A sports club can have a maximum of 15 people in each yoga class. How many classes will the club need if 87 people sign up for yoga?

    A. Divide 87 by 15. The answer is 5 with 12 left over. So the club will need 5 classes.

    B. Multiply 87 by 15. The answer is 1,218. So the club will need 1,218 classes.

    C. Divide 87 by 15. The answer is 5 with 12 left over. So the club will need 6 classes.

    D. Multiply 87 by 15. The answer is 1,305. So the club will need 1,305 classes.

12. The farmworkers put 12 eggs in each box. They boxed 3,364 eggs in one month. How many complete boxes did the workers fill?

    A. Divide 3,364 by 12. The answer is 280 with 4 left over. The farmworkers filled 281 boxes.

    B. Divide 3,364 by 12. The answer is 280 with 4 left over. The farmworkers filled 280 boxes.

    C. Divide 3,364 by 12. The answer is 28 with 4 left over. The farmworkers filled 29 boxes.

    D. Divide 3,364 by 12. The answer is 276 with 5 left over. The farmworkers filled 277 boxes.

TRY IT

State Solutions Clearly (B)

Work-Backward Strategy

Worked Examples

You can use the work-backward strategy to solve a story problem.

PROBLEM Layla has an eye appointment at 9:30 a.m. tomorrow. She needs to be there 15 minutes early to fill out forms. It takes her 30 minutes to get ready in the morning and she needs to allow 25 minutes to get to the eye doctor's office from home. At what time should Layla start getting ready tomorrow?

Solve. Then explain how you solved the problem

SOLUTION

UNDERSTAND THE PROBLEM The ending time is given (9:30 a.m.) and the starting time needs to be found. (The starting time is when Layla needs to start getting ready.)

DEVISE A PLAN Work backward. Start at the time Layla must be at the doctor's office. Then move back the number of minutes it takes each event to happen to find what time she should start getting ready.

CARRY OUT THE PLAN Start at the ending time and move back by subtracting the minutes Layla will spend on each event.

start here
↓

8:20 a.m. ← minus 30 min ← 8:50 a.m. ← minus 25 min ← 9:15 a.m. ← minus 15 min ← 9:30 a.m.

So 8:20 a.m. is the time Layla should start getting ready.

LOOK BACK To be sure the answer makes sense, write the answer, 8:20 a.m., on the far left. Add the minutes for each event, moving to the right. Since the result is 9:30 a.m., then the answer of 8:20 a.m. is correct.

8:20 a.m. → plus 30 min → 8:50 a.m. → plus 25 min → 9:15 a.m. → plus 15 min → 9:30 a.m.

ANSWER Layla should start getting ready at 8:20 a.m. To solve the problem, you start at the ending time. You subtract the minutes Layla spent on each event, recording the time before each event. The final time you record is the time Layla should start getting ready.

LEARN

Solve. Then explain how you solved the problem.

1. Carl started with some money in his savings account. He withdrew $30 and then deposited $75. Next, he deposited $40 and withdrew $50. Now he has $148. How much money did Carl start with in his savings account?

2. Some people were at the museum when it opened at 10:00 a.m. By noon, 98 people had entered the museum and 32 people had left. From noon until 8:00 p.m., 128 more people arrived and 79 left. At 8:00 p.m., 200 people remained in the museum. How many people were at the museum when it opened?

Read the problem and follow the directions.

3. Write a three- or four-sentence story problem that uses the information in the table. Then work backward to solve the problem.

Movie title	Start times	Length of movie
Shark Attack	1:30 p.m., 4:30 p.m., 7:00 p.m.	109 minutes
Friends in Space	1:15 p.m., 3:50 p.m., 6:30 p.m.	117 minutes
Playground Capers	1:25 p.m., 4:45 p.m., 7:15 p.m.	110 minutes
Mystery Mission	1:20 p.m., 4:15 p.m., 6:45 p.m.	98 minutes

LEARN

Problem-Solving Strategies

Select the Strategy

For each story problem, some problem-solving strategies are more helpful than others. Before you devise a plan, you need to look for strategies that will help you correctly solve the problem. You also need to identify strategies that will not help you correctly solve the problem.

PROBLEM Which strategy would **not** correctly solve this story problem?

- Trent wants to get a cell phone. The phone costs $50. Cell phone service costs $42 a month. How much money does Trent need to get a cell phone and service for 6 months?

A. Make a table.

Month	1	2	3	4	5	6
Total cost	$92	$134	$176	$218	$260	?

B. Make a line graph.

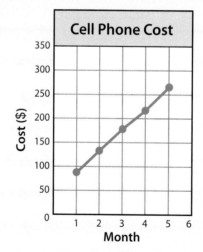

C. Write an equation. ⟶ $50 + (42 \times 6) = m$

D. Make a model. ⟶ Take 42 pieces of play money.
Divide the money into 6 equal groups.
Add $50 to each group.

SOLUTION

UNDERSTAND THE PROBLEM You need to find out which strategy would **not** correctly solve this story problem.

DEVISE A PLAN Look at each answer choice and ask yourself, "Will this strategy correctly solve this story problem? Why or why not?" The answer choice that will **not** correctly solve this story problem is the correct answer.

CARRY OUT THE PLAN
- **Answer choice A.** Yes, the table shows the amount Trent would spend each month and includes the cost of the phone and the monthly service fee. If you complete the table, you will find the amount spent in 6 months.
- **Answer choice B.** Yes, the graph shows a linear relationship because the same amount, or $42, is spent each month after the first month. If you extend the straight line with a straightedge, you will find the amount that will be spent in 6 months.
- **Answer choice C.** Yes, the monthly fee is $42, so the monthly fee for 6 months is $42 × 6. Add this to the cost of the cell phone ($50) to get the equation $50 + (42 \times 6) = m$. If you solve this equation, you will find the amount that will be spent in 6 months.
- **Answer choice D.** No, this model shows division instead of multiplication. It would **not** correctly solve this problem, so it is the correct answer choice.

LOOK BACK Make sure you've answered the question that was asked. Have you found the answer choice that will **not** correctly solve this story problem?

ANSWER Answer choice D is the correct answer to the question, "Which strategy does **not** correctly solve this story problem?"

Choose the strategy that would **not** correctly solve the problem.

1. Samantha notices that it is 2:15 p.m. now. Her friend Shelly called her 30 minutes ago. At that time, Shelly told Samantha that she had left home in another city 2 hours and 45 minutes earlier to come visit. What time did Shelly leave home?

   A. **Work backward.** The end time is 2:15 p.m. Subtract (go back) 30 minutes. Then subtract (go back) 2 hours and 45 minutes to find the start time.

   B. **Look for a pattern.**
      2 hours 15 minutes
      0 minutes
      2 hours 45 minutes

   C. **Guess and test.** Guess a time before 2:15 and then check if it works with the information in the problem. Add 2 hours 45 minutes to the time and then add another 30 minutes. If the end time is 2:15 p.m., the start time is correct.

   D. **Make a model.** Use or draw a clock to model the problem. Set the time to 2:15. Then move the minute hand back half a turn to show 30 minutes. This is the time of the phone call. Then move the minute hand back again to show 45 minutes. Move the hour hand back 2 numbers to show the 2 hours. The time shown is the start time.

LEARN

Choose the strategy that would not correctly solve the problem.

2. Helen had some pocket money. Her sister had $6, and Helen had twice as much money as her sister. Helen spent $2 at the post office and $3 at the newspaper store. How much money did Helen have left?

   A. **Use objects to model the problem.** Take 6 pieces of play money. Take away 2 pieces and then take away 3 pieces.

   B. **Draw a diagram.** Draw 6 dots to represent how much money Helen's sister has. Draw 12 dots to show how much money Helen has. Cross out 2 of Helen's dots to represent the money she spent at the post office. Cross out 3 of Helen's dots to represent the money she spent at the newspaper store. Circle the remaining dots in Helen's group.

   C. **Use logical reasoning.** Multiply 6 by 2 to figure out how much money Helen has to begin with. The answer is 12. Subtract 2 from 12 for the money Helen spent at the post office. The answer is 10. Subtract 3 from 10 for the money Helen spent at the newspaper store.

   D. **Translate into an equation.** $(6 \times 2) - (3 + 2) = n$

Choose the strategy that would correctly solve the story problem.

3. A square game board has 4 small squares in each row and 4 small squares in each column. How would you shade the small squares so that each row and each column has 2 and only 2 small squares shaded?

   A. **Use logical reasoning.** If the square game board has 4 squares in each row and column, then to have 2 squares shaded in each row and column, shade 1 square in each row and 1 square in each column.

   B. **Draw a diagram.** On grid paper, draw a square that is 4 squares wide and 4 squares long. Shade 2 squares in each row. Check if the diagram shows 2 and only 2 small squares shaded in each column. Repeat if it does not. Continue until you find a combination that matches the information in the problem.

   C. **Write an equation.** $(4 \times 4) \div 2 = x$

LEARN

Problem-Solving Strategies

Different Strategies

Choose the strategy that would **not** correctly solve the problem.

1. Susie bought a sandwich and an iced tea each day at work. Each sandwich cost $4 and each iced tea cost $2. How much money did Susie spend in 7 days?

   A. **Write an equation.**
   $$(7 \times 4) + (7 \times 2) = d$$

   B. **Make a coordinate graph.**

   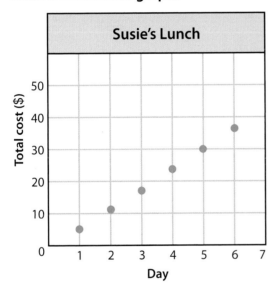

   C. **Make a table.**

   Susie's Lunch

Day	1	2	3	4	5	6	7
Total cost ($)	$6	$12	$18	$24	$30	$36	?

   D. **Use objects to model the problem.** Take 4 pieces of play money. Divide the money into 2 equal groups. Add $7 to each group.

TRY IT

Choose the strategy that would not correctly solve the problem.

2. There are 21 children at the summer camp. There are 2 times as many boys as girls. How many boys are there at the summer camp?

   A. **Draw a diagram.** Draw 21 dots. Divide the group into 3 equal groups. Draw a rectangle around 2 of the groups. Count the number of dots inside the rectangle.

   B. **Use logical reasoning.** To find out how many children at the summer camp are boys, divide the total number into 3 groups, which gives 7 in each group. As there are twice as many boys as girls, multiply 7 by 2 to get 14.

   C. **Write an equation.**
   $(21 \div 3) \times 2 = b$

   D. **Work backward.** There are 21 children at the camp. There are twice as many boys as girls, so divide by 2 to find out how many boys are at the summer camp.

3. Annie made $460 one summer. She spent $40 on some camping equipment, she spent twice as much on a new bicycle, and she spent half of what was left on her vacation. How much money did Annie spend on her vacation?

   A. **Use logical reasoning.** Start with $460. Subtract $40 to get $420. Multiply $40 by 2 to get the amount spent on the bicycle. Subtract $80 from $420 to get $340. Divide $340 by 2 to get the amount Annie spent on her vacation.

   B. **Draw a diagram.** Draw 46 tallies, one for each $10 Annie earned. Cross out 4 tallies for the $40 she spent on camping equipment. Cross out 8 tallies for the $80 spent on the bicycle. Circle half of the remaining tallies and multiply the number by $10.

   C. **Write an equation.**
   $460 - (\$40 + \$40 \times 2) = \$340$
   $340 \div 2 = m$

   D. **Guess and test.** Guess that Annie spent $100 on her vacation. Add $40 + $80 to $100 to get $220. Then multiply by 2.

TRY IT

4. Victor is raising money for charity. He raises $4 for each mile he runs and $2 for each mile he rides his bike. How much money will Victor raise if he runs for 5 miles and rides his bike for 10 miles?

A. **Use logical reasoning.**
Step 1: Multiply $4 by 5 to figure out how much money Victor makes from running.
Step 2: Then multiply $2 by 10 to figure out how much money Victor makes from riding his bike.
Step 3: Add the two products together.

B. **Write an equation.**
$(4 \times 5) + (2 \times 10) = r$

C. **Use objects to model the problem.** Use play money.
Make 5 groups of $4. Make 10 groups of $2. Add up the money.

D. **Draw a diagram.** Draw 2 circles. In one write $4 and in the other write $2. Draw a large circle around both of them to show how much money Victor makes.

5. Kelly invited 120 people to the wedding. Thirty of them were her family members. Twenty-five of them were her husband's family members, and the rest were friends of the family. How many friends of the family were invited to the wedding?

A. **Write an equation.**
$120 - (30 + 25) = f$

B. **Use logical reasoning.** Add together the number of Kelly's family (30) and the number of her husband's family (25) to find the total number of family members. Subtract this from 120 (the number of people invited) to find the number of family friends invited.

C. **Work backward.** Start with 120. Subtract 30 (the number of people from Kelly's family). Then subtract 25 (the number of people from her husband's family). The number left is the number of family friends who were invited.

D. **Draw a diagram.** Draw 12 tallies, each one representing 10 guests. Cross out 3 tallies and then cross out 2 tallies. Multiply the number of tallies left by 10.

Choose the strategy that would not correctly solve the problem.

6. Charlotte had some pineapples to sell at the fruit stand. Her friend gave her another 4 pineapples to sell. Charlotte sold 12 pineapples and had 10 pineapples left over. How many pineapples did Charlotte have to begin with?

   A. **Draw a diagram.** Draw 10 pineapples. Draw 12 pineapples for the pineapples that were sold, and cross out 4 pineapples for the ones Charlotte's friend gave her. Count how many are left over to find the number Charlotte had to begin with.

   B. **Work backward.** Start with the number of pineapples that Charlotte has left (10). Add the pineapples that were sold (12) and take away the pineapples that Charlotte's friend gave her (4).

   C. **Use logical reasoning.** Charlotte had 10 pineapples left. Her friend gave her 4, so add 4. She sold 12, so subtract 12.

   D. **Write an equation.**
      $10 + 12 - 4 = p$

Core Focus
Patterns

Explore Patterns

Solve.

1. There are 4 children at the swimming pool to start. Every hour, 10 more children arrive.

   (a) Let h = number of hours, and let n = number of children. Explain how the equation $4 + (h \times 10) = n$ shows what is happening in the problem.

   (b) Complete the table.

Hours (h)	Equation	Number of children (n)
0	$4 + (0 \times 10) = n$	4
1	$4 + (? \times 10) = n$	?
2	$4 + (? \times 10) = n$	?
3	$4 + (? \times 10) = n$	?

   (c) How many children will be at the swimming pool after 4 hours? Explain.

2. The rule to get the next term in a pattern is "Add 9."

   (a) Starting at 9, create a pattern that follows the rule. List the first 10 terms of the pattern.

   (b) Which terms in the pattern are even? Is there a pattern for where even numbers occur? Explain.

   (c) Will the 50th term of the pattern be odd or even? Explain.

TRY IT

Solve.

3.

    (a) Sketch the next 4 terms in the pattern.

    (b) What shape will the 30th term be? Explain your reasoning.

    (c) Payton says that the 100th term of the pattern will be a triangle. Is Payton correct? Explain why he is correct or why he is not correct.

4. Rule: Add a top row that has one more dot than the top row of the term before it.

    (a) Sketch the next 2 terms of the pattern.

    (b) Make a table to show how many dots will be in the top row of each of the first 5 terms of the pattern.

    (c) How many dots will be in the top row of the eighth term? Explain how you know.

    (d) Make one additional observation about the pattern.

Think Like a Mathematician Self-Check

5. State the actions and thinking you used during this lesson as a math learner.

Math Thinking and Actions

I made sense of problems by
  • Explaining to myself what a problem means and what it asks for
  • Using drawings or diagrams to represent a problem I was solving

I explained my math thinking clearly.
I tried out new ways to check if an answer is reasonable.
Other

TRY IT

Define and Sketch Triangles

Classify Triangles

Solve.

1. What is the name of a triangle that has only 2 of its 3 sides the same length?

2. How is an acute triangle different from both an obtuse triangle and a right triangle?

Name the triangle by its angles and its side lengths.

3.
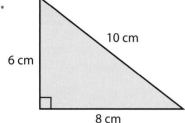
10 cm
6 cm
8 cm

4.
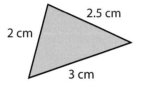
2.5 cm
2 cm
3 cm

5.
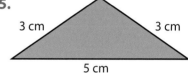
3 cm
3 cm
5 cm

Draw.

6. Use a ruler and an index card to draw an obtuse scalene triangle.

7. Use a ruler to draw an equilateral triangle.

8. Use a ruler to draw an acute isosceles triangle.

Choose the answer.

9. Which best describes an equilateral triangle?

   A. All sides are the same length; all angles have the same measure.

   B. Two sides are the same length; 1 angle measures 90°.

   C. Two sides are the same length; all angles measure less than 90°.

   D. Two sides are the same length; 1 angle measures greater than 90°.

10. Which best describes a right isosceles triangle?

   A. Two sides are the same length; 1 angle measures 90°.

   B. All sides are the same length; 2 angles measure 90°.

   C. All sides are different lengths; 1 angle measures 90°.

   D. Two sides are the same length; 1 angle measures greater than 90°.

TRY IT

Choose the answer.

11. Which triangle always has 1 right angle and 2 sides the same length?

    A. acute isosceles

    B. right isosceles

    C. right equilateral

    D. acute scalene

12. Which triangle always has all sides different lengths and all angles measuring less than 90°?

    A. obtuse equilateral

    B. acute scalene

    C. equilateral

    D. obtuse isosceles

13. Which seems to best describe this triangle?

    A. All sides are the same length; all angles are the same.

    B. Two sides are the same length; 1 angle measures 90°.

    C. Two sides are the same length; all angles are less than 90°.

    D. Two sides are the same length; 1 angle is obtuse.

14. Which appears to be an equilateral triangle?

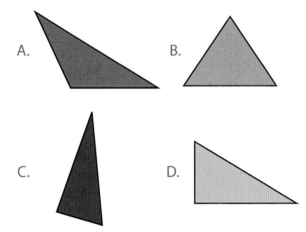

    A.

    B.

    C.

    D.

15. Which name correctly classifies this triangle?

3 in.   3 in.

2.5 in.

    A. acute isosceles

    B. obtuse equilateral

    C. acute scalene

    D. obtuse isosceles

16. Which name correctly classifies this triangle?

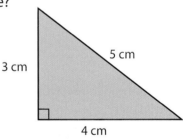

3 cm   5 cm

4 cm

    A. right isosceles

    B. obtuse equilateral

    C. acute scalene

    D. right scalene

TRY IT

Define and Sketch Quadrilaterals (A)

Identify Quadrilaterals

Answer the question.

1. How are these two shapes alike and how are they different?

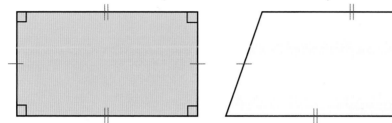

2. How are these two shapes alike and how are they different?

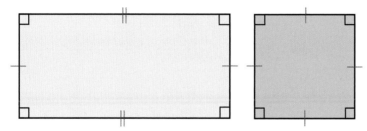

Read the problem and follow the directions.

3. Use a ruler to draw a parallelogram and a trapezoid. Explain how these two shapes are alike and how they are different.

4. Use a ruler to draw a rectangle and a square. Explain how these two shapes are alike and how they are different.

Choose the answer.

5. Which shape has one pair of opposite sides that are parallel but not equal in length?

   A. parallelogram
   B. square
   C. trapezoid
   D. rhombus

6. Which statement is true for all rectangles?

   A. All sides are equal in length.
   B. All angles are right angles.
   C. All angles are acute.
   D. Two angles are obtuse and 2 angles are acute.

TRY IT

Choose the answer.

7. Which best describes this quadrilateral?

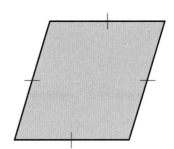

A. polygon with all right angles

B. polygon with exactly 1 pair of sides that are equal in length

C. polygon with exactly 1 pair of parallel sides

D. polygon with 4 sides that are equal in length

8. Which shape has opposite sides that are both equal in length and parallel?

A. triangle

B. trapezoid

C. pentagon

D. parallelogram

9. Which shape has 4 congruent sides?

A. circle

B. trapezoid

C. rhombus

D. triangle

10. Choose **all** the names that could be used to classify this shape.

A. quadrilateral

B. trapezoid

C. parallelogram

D. rectangle

11. Choose **all** the names that could be used to classify this shape.

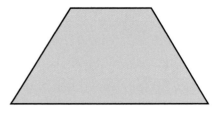

A. rhombus

B. parallelogram

C. quadrilateral

D. trapezoid

TRY IT

Line Symmetry

Find Lines of Symmetry

Choose the answer.

1. Which figures have line symmetry?

A.    B.    C.   D.

2. Which figures have line symmetry?

A.   B.   C.    D.

3. Which pictures have line symmetry?

A.    B.

C.   D.

4. Which letters have line symmetry?

A.   B. E   C. K   D. M

TRY IT

Choose the answer.

5. How many lines of symmetry does this rectangle have?

A. 0

B. 2

C. 3

D. 4

6. How many lines of symmetry does this square have?

A. 6

B. 5

C. 4

D. 3

7. How many lines of symmetry does this butterfly have?

A. 1

B. 2

C. 4

D. 6

8. How many lines of symmetry does this letter have?

A. 0

B. 1

C. 2

D. 4

T R Y   I T

Practice Quadrilateral Angles

Solve.

1. A quadrilateral has angles that measure 77°, 108°, and 65°
   What is the measure of the fourth angle?

2. A quadrilateral has angles that measure 91°, 96°, and 88°.
   What is the measure of the fourth angle?

3. A quadrilateral has angles that measure 87°, 69°, and 104°.
   What is the measure of the fourth angle?

4. What is the measure of ∠K?

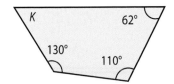

5. What is the measure of ∠B?

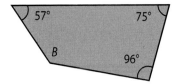

6. What is the measure of ∠S?

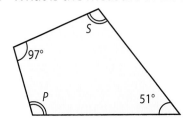

7. What is the measure of ∠E?

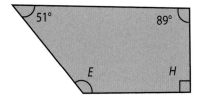

Choose the answer.

8. What is the measure of ∠C?

   A. 83°   B. 93°

   C. 103°   D. 123°

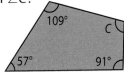

9. What is the measure of ∠C?

   A. 68°   B. 78°

   C. 88°   D. 98°

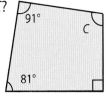

10. What is the measure of ∠F?

   A. 97°   B. 101°

   C. 111°   D. 121°

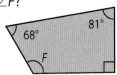

T R Y   I T

Expressions and Equations

Algebraic Expressions and Equations

Worked Examples

You can use variables to write algebraic expressions or equations that match different descriptions. You can use any symbol to stand for the unknown number. For example, you can use a triangle (▲) for the variable.

PROBLEM 1 Write an expression that matches this situation:

- Katherine separates a pile of photos into five equal groups.

SOLUTION

UNDERSTAND THE PROBLEM
You are separating an unknown number of photos into 5 equal groups, or dividing an unknown number by 5.

DEVISE A PLAN Use (▲) to stand for the unknown number of photos.

CARRY OUT THE PLAN
▲ ÷ 5

LOOK BACK Make sure you've answered what was asked. Katherine separates photos into 5 equal groups, so the following expression makes sense: ▲ ÷ 5.

ANSWER ▲ ÷ 5

PROBLEM 2 Write an equation that matches this situation:

- Leo had some batteries and then bought six more. He has thirteen batteries now.

SOLUTION

UNDERSTAND THE PROBLEM
"Bought six more" means addition, so you are adding 6 to an unknown number of batteries. "He has thirteen batteries now" means "equals 13."

DEVISE A PLAN Use (▲) to stand for the unknown number of batteries.

CARRY OUT THE PLAN
▲ + 6 = 13

LOOK BACK Make sure you've answered what was asked. Leo had some batteries and bought 6 more for a total of 13 batteries. So the following equation makes sense: ▲ + 6 = 13.

ANSWER ▲ + 6 = 13

Read the situation. Use a triangle (▲) for the variable and explain what the variable represents. Then write the algebraic expression or equation that matches the situation.

1. Toby has three times as many trading cards as Ruth.
   Toby has twenty-four cards.

2. Joe bought a bag of chips.
   He ate twelve of them.
   He has eight chips left.

3. Amy has six stacks of CDs with the same number of CDs in each stack.

Read the situation. Use a question mark (?) for the variable and explain what the variable represents. Then write the algebraic expression or equation that matches the situation.

4. Jill walks five blocks to the library and then continues on to the grocery store.
   She walks a total of fifteen blocks.

5. Nathan has thirty party favors to divide among each of his friends.

Read the situation. Use *p* for the variable and explain what the variable represents. Then write the algebraic expression or equation that matches the situation.

6. Lizzy scored twelve points in each basketball game this season.
   She scored a total of eighty-four points.

7. Adam had a bag of rocks.
   He lost eleven of them.
   He now has twenty-five rocks.

LEARN

Expressions and Equations

Expressions and Equations Practice

Read the situation. Then write the expression or equation that matches the situation. To represent an unknown number, use a symbol or letter.

1. Write an expression that means twelve times an unknown number.

2. Lisa took twenty-five pictures on her digital camera. She deleted twelve of them. She then had thirteen pictures left on her camera. Write an equation that represents this situation.

3. Write an expression that represents the following:
   Jack had some peanuts in a bag. He ate nine of the peanuts.

4. Write an equation that represents the following:
   Janet has many pairs of shoes. She bought three more pairs. She now has sixteen pairs of shoes.

5. Write an expression that represents the following:
   There are 5 flowers in each of 6 vases.

Choose the answer.

6. Which expression means 9 more than a number?

   A. $n + 9$ B. $9 \times n$

   C. $n - 9$ D. $9 \div n$

7. Which expression means 10 less than a number?

   A. $a + 10$ B. $10 \times a$

   C. $a - 10$ D. $10 \div a$

8. Which expression means 12 divided by a number?

   A. $12 \div p$ B. $p + 12$

   C. $12 \times p$ D. $p - 12$

9. Candy divides some stamps into 4 equal groups. Which expression represents this situation?

   A. $\blacktriangle - 4$ B. $4 \times \blacktriangle$

   C. $\blacktriangle \div 4$ D. $4 + \blacktriangle$

10. Neil has 5 times as many pencils as Victor. Which expression represents this situation?

    A. $\blacktriangle - 5$ B. $5 \times \blacktriangle$

    C. $\blacktriangle \div 5$ D. $\blacktriangle + 5$

11. Which equation means that 12 decreased by a number is 4?

    A. $12 - 4 = n$ B. $12 - n = 4$

    C. $12 + 4 = n$ D. $4 \times 12 = n$

TRY IT

M

Cre

Solve

1.

2.

Ans

3.

Writ

5.

7.

Cho

9.

ALGE

12. Which equation means a number divided by thirty is equal to 3?

A. $30 + 3 = e$ B. $e \div 30 = 3$ C. $30 \times e = 3$ D. $30 - 3 = e$

13. Tim walked a number of steps around the park. Then he walked 10 more steps. He walked a total of 25 steps. Which equation represents this situation?

A. $\Box + 10 = 25$ B. $25 \times 10 = \Box$ C. $25 + 10 = \Box$ D. $10 - \Box = 25$

14. Vanessa walked the same number of miles each day for 5 days. She walked a total of 20 miles. Which equation represents this situation?

A. $20 + 5 = \Box$ B. $20 - 5 = \Box$ C. $\Box \times 5 = 20$ D. $20 \times \Box = 5$

15. Manny divided his collection of baseball cards equally among 4 of his friends. Each friend got 5 cards. Which equation represents this situation?

A. $\Box = 4 + 5$ B. $\Box = 5 \div 4$ C. $\Box \div 4 = 5$ D. $4 \times 5 = \Box$

16. Kevin had some money. He spent $8. He has $20 left. Which equation represents this situation?

A. $20 - \Box = 8$ B. $20 - 8 = \Box$ C. $\Box + 8 = 20$ D. $\Box - 8 = 20$

17. Which equation means ten increased by a number equals 22?

A. $10 + t = 22$ B. $22 + 10 = t$ C. $t - 10 = 22$ D. $t \div 10 = 22$

18. Which equation means twenty divided by a number is equal to 10?

A. $20 + d = 10$ B. $20 - d = 10$ C. $20 \div d = 10$ D. $20 \times d = 10$

19. James had some apples. He bought 5 more. Which expression represents this situation?

A. $\blacktriangle - 5$ B. $5 \times \blacktriangle$ C. $\blacktriangle \div 5$ D. $\blacktriangle + 5$

20. Bonnie divides some cherries into 8 equal groups. Which expression represents this situation?

A. $p - 8$ B. $p \div 8$ C. $p + 8$ D. $8 \times p$

TRY IT

Line Segments in the Coordinate Plane

Vertical Segment Lengths

Worked Examples

If you know the coordinates of the endpoints of a vertical line segment, you can use subtraction to find its length.

PROBLEM 1

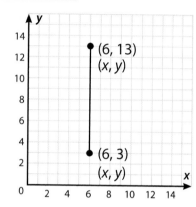

PROBLEM 2

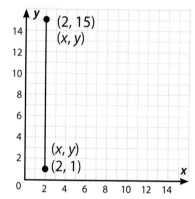

SOLUTION

1 Count the units. Then look for another way to find the length.

2 The difference between the y-coordinates, 13 and 3, also gives the length.

3 $13 - 3 = 10$
The length is 10 units.

ANSWER The length of the vertical line segment is 10 units.

SOLUTION

1 Subtract the y-coordinates, 15 and 1, to find the length. Length is always a positive number.

2 $15 - 1 = 14$
The length is 14 units.

ANSWER The length of the vertical line segment is 14 units.

Subtract to find the length of the vertical line segment. Write the subtraction equation you used. Then write the length of the segment in units.

1.

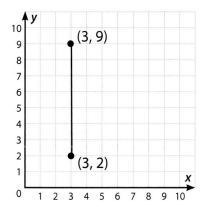

2.

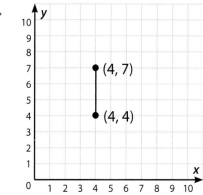

3.

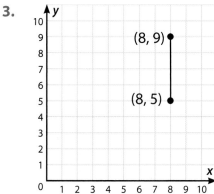

4.

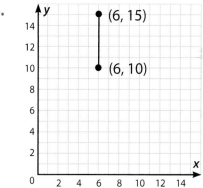

5.

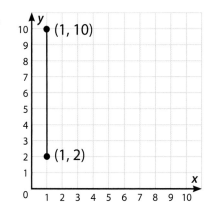

6.

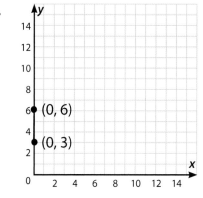

L E A R N

Linear Relationships (A)

Points on a Line

Read the problem and follow the directions.

1. Write the ordered pairs to complete the table.

$y = 3 \times x$		
Input x	**Output** y	**(Input, output)** (x, y)
0	0	?
1	3	?
2	6	?
3	9	?
4	12	?
5	15	?

2. Complete the input-output table, and then plot the points on a coordinate grid.

Rule: Subtract 3		
Input x	**Output** y	**Ordered pair** (x, y)
3	0	?
4	1	?
5	?	?
6	?	?
7	?	?
8	?	?

T R Y I T

Choose the answer.

3. Suketo plotted three points from the equation $y = 2 \times x$ on this coordinate grid. He drew a straight line through the points. Which ordered pair would also be on this line?

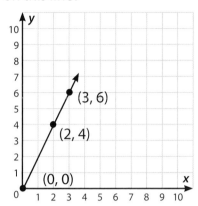

A. (3, 8)　　　　　　　B. (4, 6)

C. (5, 10)　　　　　　D. (7, 7)

4. Sari plotted three points from the equation $y = x + 4$ on this coordinate grid. She drew a straight line through the points. Which ordered pair would also be on this line?

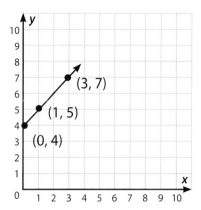

A. (3, 9)　　　　　　　B. (6, 7)

C. (3, 6)　　　　　　　D. (5, 9)

5. Identify the graph that matches the equation in the table.

y = x + 3		
Input x	Output y	Ordered pair (x, y)
0	3	(0, 3)
1	4	(1, 4)
2	5	(2, 5)
3	6	(3, 6)
4	7	(4, 7)
5	8	(5, 8)

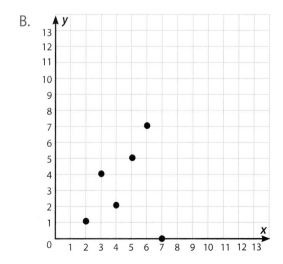

TRY IT

Linear Relationships (B)

More Straight Lines

You can write ordered pairs (x, y) from an input-output table. Then you can graph the ordered pairs on a coordinate plane and see that they lie on a straight line.

PROBLEM Use the input and output values on the table to write ordered pairs in the third column. Then plot the points on the coordinate grid.

Rule: Subtract 5 or $y = x - 5$		
Input x	Output y	(Input, output) (x, y)
5	0	?
6	1	?
7	2	?
8	3	?
9	4	?
10	5	?
11	6	?
12	7	?
13	8	?

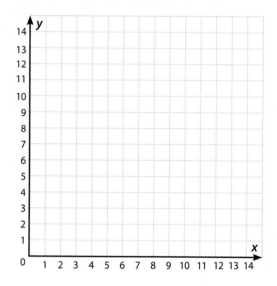

LEARN

1 To write the ordered pairs in the third column of the table, follow these steps:

- Write the value of the *x*-coordinate given in the Input column on the same row.
- Follow the *x*-coordinate with a comma, and skip a space.
- Write the value of the *y*-coordinate from the Output column on the same row.
- Enclose the coordinates with parentheses.

2 To plot the points on the coordinate grid, follow these steps:

- To plot point (5, 0), start at the origin and move right 5 units on the *x*-axis, in a positive direction. From that point, move 0 units on the *y*-axis, not moving up or down. Draw a point.
- To plot point (6, 1), start at the origin and move right 6 units on the *x*-axis, in a positive direction. From that point, move up 1 unit in a positive direction, parallel to the *y*-axis. Draw a point.
- Continue until all points have been plotted.

ANSWER

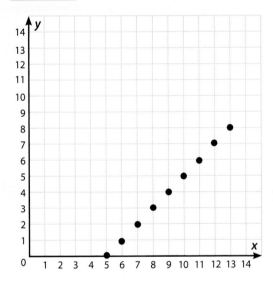

Rule: Subtract 5 or $y = x - 5$		
Input *x*	Output *y*	(Input, output) (*x*, *y*)
5	0	(5, 0)
6	1	(6, 1)
7	2	(7, 2)
8	3	(8, 3)
9	4	(9, 4)
10	5	(10, 5)
11	6	(11, 6)
12	7	(12, 7)
13	8	(13, 8)

L E A R N

Write the ordered pairs (x, y) to complete the table. Then plot the points
on the coordinate grid.

1.

Rule: Add 3 or y = x + 3		
Input x	Output y	(Input, output) (x, y)
0	3	?
1	4	?
2	5	?
3	6	?
4	7	?
5	8	?
6	9	?
7	10	?
8	11	?

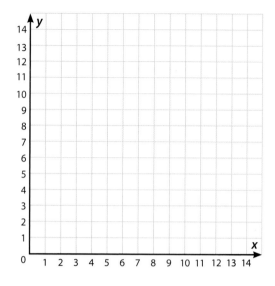

2.

Rule: Subtract 4 or y = x − 4		
Input x	Output y	(Input, output) (x, y)
14	10	?
13	9	?
12	8	?
11	7	?
10	6	?
9	5	?
8	4	?
7	3	?

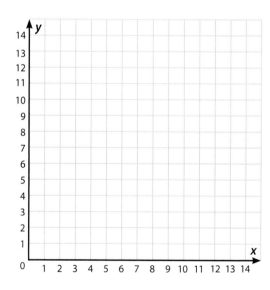

Read the problem and complete the table. Use the input values and apply the rule given in the table to write the output values in the second column and the ordered pairs in the third column. Then plot the points on the coordinate grid.

3. Serena attended camp. The number of new friends she made each day was 2 more than the number of days she was there. On Day 4, Serena made 4 + 2, or 6, new friends. Help Serena complete the table and plot the ordered pairs of (day, new friends) on the coordinate grid.

Rule: Add 2 or $y = x + 2$		
Input x	Output y	(Input, output) (x, y)
4	?	?
5	?	?
6	?	?
7	?	?
8	?	?
9	?	?
10	?	?
11	?	?

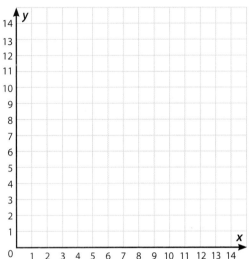

LEARN

Linear Relationships (B)

Check the Coordinates

Read the problem and follow the directions.

1. Write the ordered pairs to complete the table.

$y = x - 10$		
Input x	Output y	(Input, output) (x, y)
20	10	?
19	9	?
18	8	?
17	7	?
16	6	?
15	5	?
14	4	?

Choose the answer.

2. Joyce plotted three points from the equation $y = 3 \times x$ on this coordinate grid. She drew a straight line through the points. Which ordered pair would also be on this line?

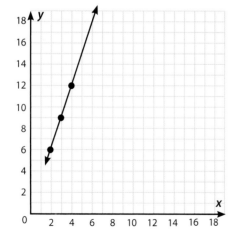

A. (0, 18)

B. (6, 6)

C. (6, 18)

D. (9, 18)

TRY IT

3. Identify the graph that matches the equation in the table.

y = x − 7		
Input x	Output y	(Input, output) (x, y)
12	5	?
11	4	?
10	3	?
9	2	?
8	1	?
7	0	?

A.
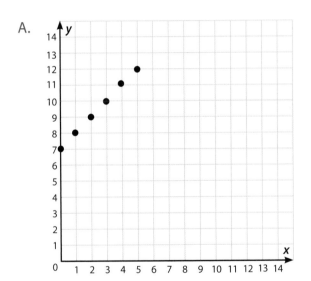

B.
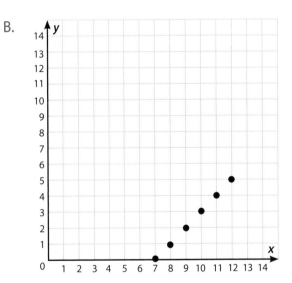

TRY IT

Choose the answer.

4. Which correctly graphs $y = x - 8$?

A.
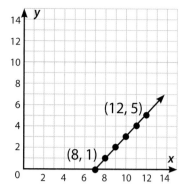

B.
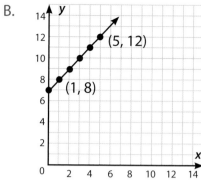

C.
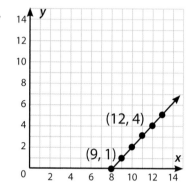

5. Which correctly graphs $y = x - 9$?

A.
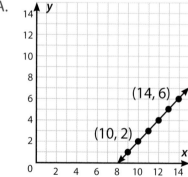

B.
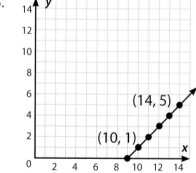

C.
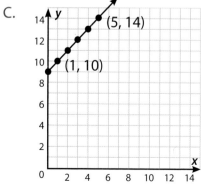

TRY IT

6. Parker plotted three points from the equation $y = x + 3$ on this coordinate grid. He drew a straight line through the points. Which ordered pair would also be on this line?

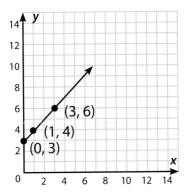

A. (1, 3)   B. (3, 3)

C. (6, 9)   D. (9, 3)

7. Jen plotted three points from the equation $y = 3 \times x + 1$ on this coordinate grid. She drew a straight line through the points. Which ordered pair would also be on this line?

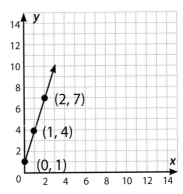

A. (3, 10)   B. (3, 3)

C. (4, 7)   D. (5, 11)

TRY IT

Ordered Pairs and Story Problems

Interpret Coordinates on a Graph

Worked Examples

You can describe what ordered pairs mean. You can explain what a graph means.

PROBLEM Stephen decided to collect 6 pieces of recyclable items every week. He wants to make a graph so he can predict the total amount of recyclable items he will pick up after 4 weeks. Create a graph with the following points to show how much he will pick up. Then interpret the points on the graph.

- W (1, 6)
- X (2, 12)
- Y (3, 18)
- Z (4, 24)

SOLUTION

1 Plot each point on a coordinate grid.

2 Interpret the graph:
- Explain what each ordered pair means.
- Explain whether or not a line should connect the points.
- Explain whether any of the ordered pairs can have a number less than or equal to 0 as a coordinate.
- Explain how seeing the graph makes it easier to understand what is happening in the story problem.

ANSWER

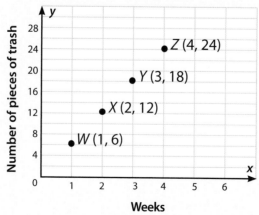

Stephen's Recycling Goals

Interpretation of the graph:

- *W* (1, 6) means that in the first week, Stephen picked up a total of 6 recyclable items.

   X (2, 12) means that in the second week, he picked up a total of 12 recyclable items.

   Y (3, 18) means that in the third week, he picked up a total of 18 recyclable items.

   Z (4, 24) means that in the fourth week, he picked up a total of 24 recyclable items.

- A line should not connect the points. It does not make sense in the problem to talk about the number of recycled items Stephen collects in $1\frac{1}{2}$ or $2\frac{1}{2}$ weeks.

- None of the ordered pairs should have a number less than or equal to 0 as a coordinate because 0 or fewer weeks and 0 or fewer recyclable items are not possible in this problem.

- The graph helps show that as the number of weeks increases, the number of recyclable items increases.

Plot the points on a Quadrant I Coordinate Grid.

1. Paul collects baseball cards. Each pack has 5 cards. Paul decides to make a graph so that he can keep track of how many cards he has. Plot the following points and ordered pairs with their labels:

   - *A* (0, 0)
   - *B* (1, 5)
   - *C* (2, 10)
   - *D* (3, 15)

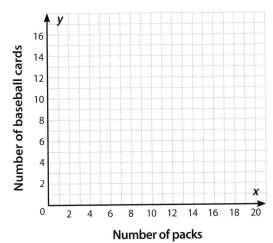

Number of Packs and Baseball Cards

Refer to the story problem and the points, ordered pairs, and labels you plotted in Problem 1 to answer the questions.

2. What does the ordered pair (0, 0) mean?

3. What does the ordered pair (1, 5) mean?

4. What does the ordered pair (2, 10) mean?

5. What does the ordered pair (3, 15) mean?

6. Can there be a negative number of baseball card packs?

7. Can there be a negative number of baseball cards?

8. What happens to the number of baseball cards as the number of packs increase?

9. What happens to the graph as the number of packs increases and the number of cards increases?

10. Does it make sense to connect the points in the graph with a line? Why?

11. How does seeing the graph make it easier to understand what is happening in the situation?

Solve.

1. Tim's family went on vacation to Yellowstone National Park. When they left, they had 15 gallons of gas. After 1 hour, they had 12 gallons of gas left. Tim made a graph of how much gas they had left after each hour so his mother could plan when she would need to stop for gas.

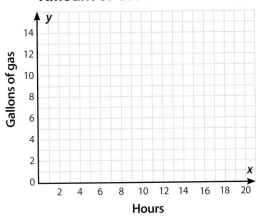

Amount of Gas and Travel Time

Gallons of gas (y-axis), Hours (x-axis)

(a) Plot the following points, ordered pairs, and labels.

A (0, 15)   B (1, 12)

C (2, 9)   D (3, 6)

E (4, 3)   F (5, 0)

(b) Connect the points with a line.

(c) Refer to the story problem and the points, ordered pairs, and labels you plotted to answer the questions.

- What does the ordered pair (0, 15) mean?

- What does the ordered pair (1, 12) mean?

- What does the ordered pair (4, 3) mean?

- What does the ordered pair (5, 0) mean?

- What happens to the gallons of gas as the hours increase?

- Does it make sense to connect the points in the graph with a line? Explain.

TRY IT

Solve.

2. Carly went to the zoo. While she was there, she kept track of how many animals she saw and how much time she'd spent there. Carly wants to make a graph so she can understand her data better.

Time at the zoo (min)	Number of animals
0	0
4	2
8	4
12	6
16	8
20	10

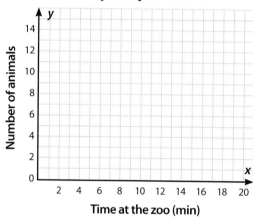

Carly's Trip to the Zoo

(a) Use the data in Carly's chart to make a list of ordered pairs for the graph.

(b) Plot and label each of the ordered pairs on the coordinate graph.

(c) Refer to the story problem and the points, ordered pairs, and labels you plotted to answer the questions.

- What does the ordered pair (0, 0) mean?

- What does the ordered pair (4, 2) mean?

- What does the ordered pair (12, 6) mean?

- What does the ordered pair (20, 10) mean?

- What happens to the number of animals Carly sees as the amount of time increases?

- Does it make sense to connect the points in the graph with a line? Explain.

Think Like a Mathematician Self-Check

3. State the actions and thinking you used during this lesson as a math learner.

Math Thinking and Actions
I made sense of problems by • Explaining to myself what a problem means and what it asks for • Using drawings or diagrams to represent a problem I was solving
I explained my math thinking clearly.
I tried out new ways to check if an answer is reasonable.
Other

TRY IT

Perimeters of Polygons

Measure Perimeter

Worked Examples

You can use a ruler to find the perimeter of a polygon. First you measure each side of the outside border of the figure. Be sure to measure with the unit mentioned in the problem, centimeters or inches. Then you find the sum of the lengths of the sides and include the unit in your answer.

PROBLEM Use a dual-scale ruler to find the perimeter of this figure in centimeters.

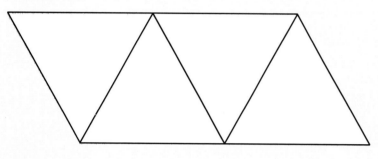

SOLUTION

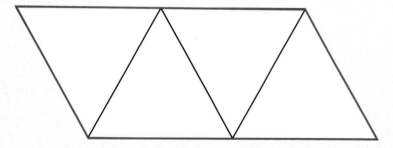

1 Use the metric edge of a dual-scale ruler.

2 Measure each side of the outside border of the figure. Record each measure.
- upper side, 8 cm
- right side, 4 cm
- lower side, 8 cm
- left side, 4 cm

3 Find the sum of the lengths of the sides.

ANSWER The perimeter of the figure is 24 centimeters.

Use a dual-scale ruler to solve.

1. What is the perimeter of this figure in centimeters?

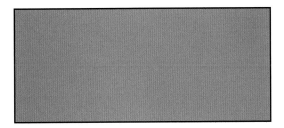

2. What is the perimeter of this figure in inches?

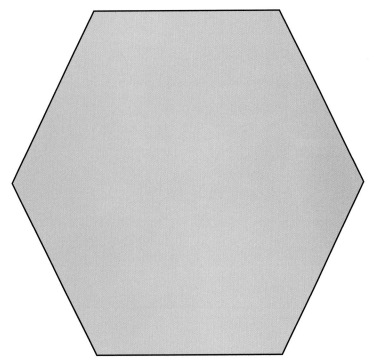

L E A R N

Use a dual-scale ruler to solve.

3. What is the perimeter of this figure in centimeters?

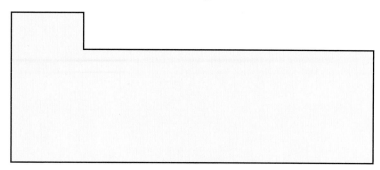

4. What is the perimeter of this figure in inches?

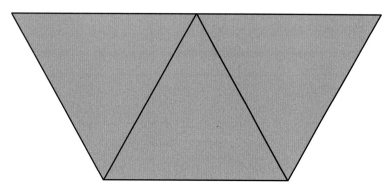

5. What is the perimeter of the shaded part of this figure in centimeters?

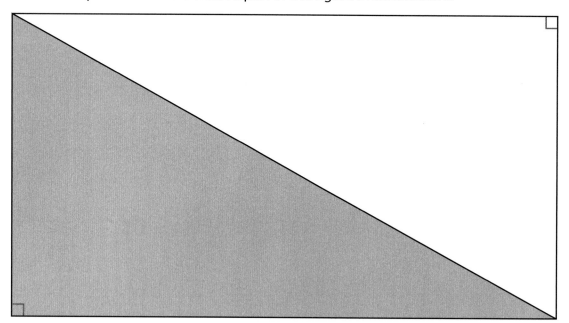

LEARN

Perimeters of Polygons

Perimeter Practice

Use a ruler to find the perimeter of the figure in centimeters.

1.

2.

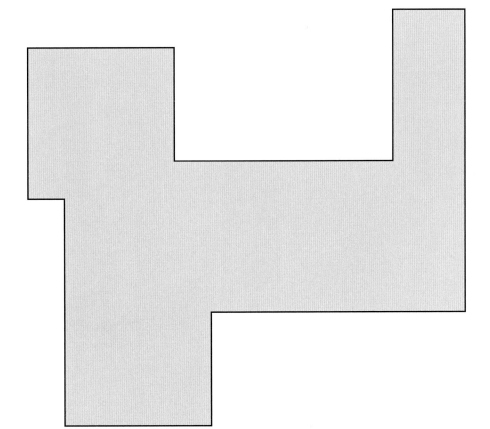

TRY IT

Use a ruler to find the perimeter of the figure in inches.

3.

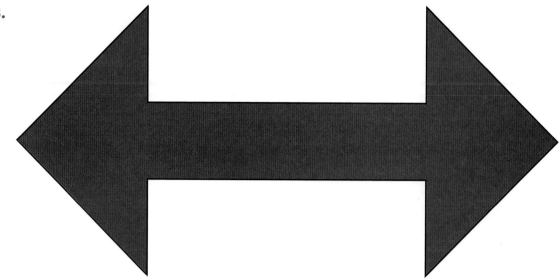

Solve.

4. The rectangle and the hexagon have the same perimeter.
   What are the lengths of the sides of the rectangle that are unmarked?

7 yd

7 yd

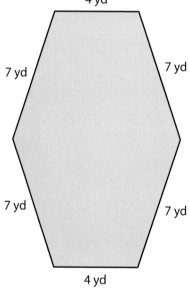

4 yd

7 yd   7 yd

7 yd   7 yd

4 yd

5. What is the perimeter of this parallelogram?

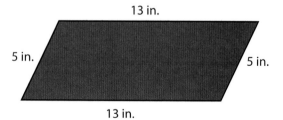

13 in.

5 in.   5 in.

13 in.

TRY IT

Choose the answer.

6. The length of one side of the square is equal to the length of 6 arrows. If each arrow represents 1 unit, what is the perimeter of the square?

   A. 6 units   B. 18 units

   C. 24 units   D. 36 units

7. What is the perimeter of the shaded rectangle on this grid?

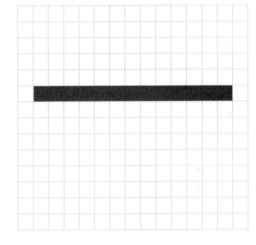

   A. 13 units   B. 14 units

   C. 26 units   D. 28 units

8. What is the perimeter of this polygon?

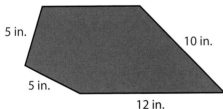

   A. 30 in.   B. 32 in.

   C. 35 in.   D. 40 in.

9. What is the perimeter of the polygon if each side is 6 cm?

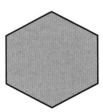

   A. 1 cm   B. 12 cm

   C. 30 cm   D. 36 cm

10. The base of Jill's house is in the shape of a regular octagon. Each side of the octagon measures 25 feet. Find the perimeter of the base of Jill's house.

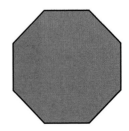

   A. 100 ft   B. 150 ft

   C. 200 ft   D. 250 ft

TRY IT

Choose the answer.

11. Which triangle has the same perimeter as the green triangle?

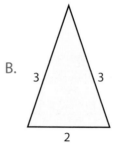

4 3 2

A.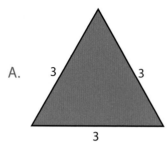

3   3

3

B.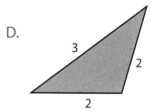

3   3

2

C.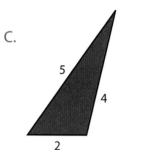

5

4

2

D.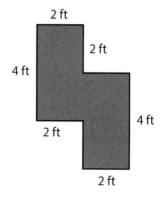

3

2

2

12. The triangle has the same perimeter as the square.

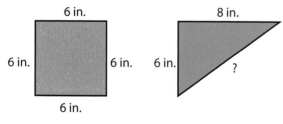

6 in.

6 in.   6 in.

6 in.

8 in.

6 in.   ?

What is the length of the unknown side of the triangle?

A. 6 in.

B. 10 in.

C. 14 in.

D. 24 in.

13. All angles shown on the figure are right angles. What is the perimeter of the figure?

2 ft

2 ft

4 ft

2 ft

4 ft

2 ft

A. 16 ft

B. 18 ft

C. 20 ft

D. 22 ft

TRY IT

14. Michele is looking for a rug with a perimeter of 24 feet. Which rectangular rug has a perimeter of 24 feet?

A.

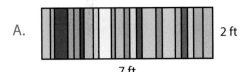

2 ft

7 ft

B.

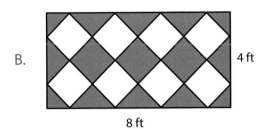

4 ft

8 ft

C.

2 ft

12 ft

D.

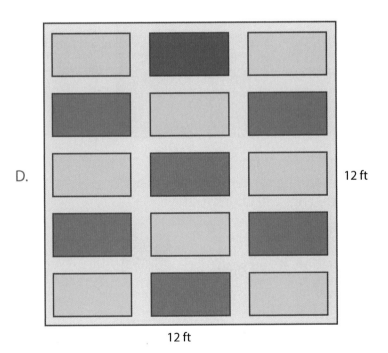

12 ft

12 ft

TRY IT

Formulas for Perimeter (A)

Find the Perimeters

Solve.

1. What is the perimeter of this rectangle?

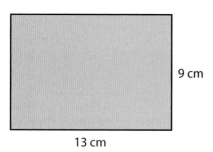

9 cm

13 cm

2. What is the perimeter of this rectangle?

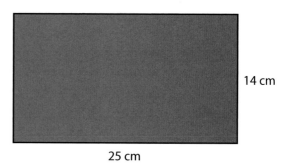

14 cm

25 cm

3. What is the perimeter of this square?

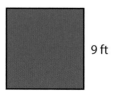

9 ft

4. What is the perimeter of this square?

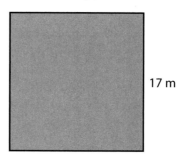

17 m

5. Chuck wants to put a fence around his square garden. One side of his garden measures 3 meters. How much fence will Chuck need?

Find the perimeter. Use a formula, or equation, if you wish.
Note: Diagrams are not drawn to scale.

6.

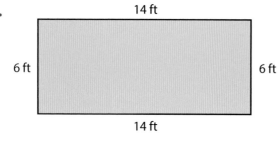

14 ft

6 ft   6 ft

14 ft

7.

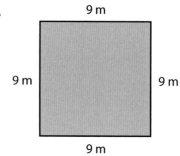

9 m

9 m   9 m

9 m

T R Y   I T

8.

35 cm

6 cm   6 cm

35 cm

9.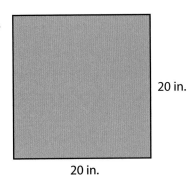

20 in.

20 in.

Choose the answer.

10. Jordan needs to find the perimeter of a large rectangular table represented by the sketch. Which statement describes how she could correctly calculate the perimeter?

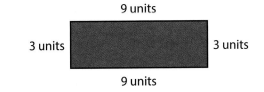

9 units

3 units   3 units

9 units

A. Add 9 + 3.

B. Multiply 9 × 3.

C. Add 9 + 9 + 3 + 3.

D. Multiply 9 × 9 × 3 × 3.

11. Mrs. Vasquez needs to determine the perimeter of the rectangular window shown so she can buy wood trim to go around it. Which equation could Mrs. Vasquez use to determine the perimeter of the window?

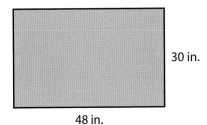

30 in.

48 in.

A. $P = 48 \times 30$

B. $P = 48 + 30$

C. $P = 48 + 30 + 48$

D. $P = 48 + 48 + 30 + 30$

12. What is the perimeter of the rectangle?

A. 11 ft

B. 20 ft

C. 22 ft

D. 28 ft

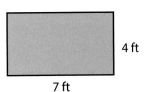

4 ft

7 ft

T R Y   I T

Choose the answer.

13. Aldo folded a paper in half, then he cut out a rectangle along the fold. What is the perimeter of the cut rectangle when it is unfolded?

  A. 5 in.

  B. 7 in.

  C. 10 in.

  D. 14 in.

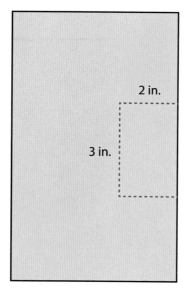

2 in.

3 in.

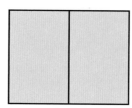

14. Mrs. Anderson wants to install a fence around her square yard. One side of the yard measures 36 feet. How much feet of fencing does she need?

  A. 72 ft

  B. 144 ft

  C. 288 ft

  D. 1,296 ft

Read the problem and follow the directions.

15. Maria used this formula to find the perimeter of a rectangular game board:

  $(2 \times 5) + (2 \times 8) = 26$; Perimeter is 26 inches.

  Sketch and label Maria's game board. Then write another equation that you can use to find the perimeter of the game board.

TRY IT

Formulas for Perimeter (B)

Apply Perimeter Formulas

Worked Examples

You can use formulas to find the perimeter of geometric shapes. First you draw and label a diagram. Then you write a formula and replace the variables with the dimensions from the diagram. Next you compute the perimeter.

PROBLEM 1 What is the perimeter of a rectangular picture frame with these dimensions?

9 in.

12 in.

SOLUTION 1

Add the lengths of the sides to find the perimeter of a rectangle.

$P = l + l + w + w$
$P = 12 + 12 + 9 + 9$
$P = 42$

ANSWER The perimeter of the picture frame is 42 inches.

SOLUTION 2

Add (2 × length) + (2 × width) to find the perimeter of a rectangle.

$P = (2 \times l) + (2 \times w)$
$P = (2 \times 12) + (2 \times 9)$
$P = 24 + 18$
$P = 42$

ANSWER The perimeter of the picture frame is 42 inches.

Complete the equation to find the perimeter of the figure.

1.

8 ft

6 ft

$P = l + w + l + w$
$P = \underline{?} + 6 + 8 + \underline{?}$
$P = \underline{?}$

The perimeter is $\underline{?}$ feet.

L E A R N

Write a perimeter formula for the figure. Replace the variables in your formula with the corresponding given measures. Then find the perimeter.

2. The rectangle below has a width of 5 centimeters and a length of 22 centimeters.

3.

9 m

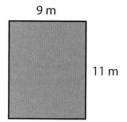

11 m

4.

45 m

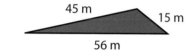

15 m

56 m

5.

99 yd

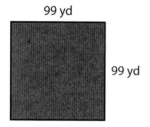

99 yd

Solve.

6. Trudy sewed together two quilt squares like the ones shown. She then put fringe around the outside of the new rectangular piece of material. How many inches of fringe did Trudy use?

13 in.

13 in. 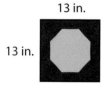 13 in.   13 in. 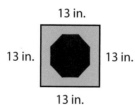 13 in.

13 in.

13 in.

13 in.

13 in.

7. Stephen folds a piece of cardboard and then cuts out a triangle as shown. What is the perimeter of the triangular piece of cardboard?

6 cm

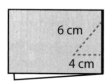

4 cm

PERIMETER AND AREA FORMULAS

FORMULAS FOR PERIMETER (B)

Worked Examples

You can use formulas to find the perimeter of geometric shapes. First you draw and label a diagram. Then you write a formula and replace the variables with the dimensions from the diagram. Next you compute the perimeter.

PROBLEM 2 Karl wants to put a fence around a rectangular garden that is 6 feet by 9 feet. How long should the fence be?

6 ft

9 ft

SOLUTION 1

❶ Draw and label a diagram.

❷ Use the perimeter formula $P = (2 \times l) + (2 \times w)$.

$P = (2 \times l) + (2 \times w)$
$P = (2 \times 9) + (2 \times 6)$
$P = 18 + 12$
$P = 30$

ANSWER The perimeter is 30 feet, so the fence will be 30 feet long.

SOLUTION 2

❶ Draw and label a diagram.

❷ Use the perimeter formula $P = 2 \times (l + w)$.

$P = 2 \times (l + w)$
$P = 2 \times (9 + 6)$
$P = 2 \times 15$
$P = 30$

ANSWER The perimeter is 30 feet, so the fence will be 30 feet long.

Complete the equation to solve.

8. A swimming pool is a rectangle 100 feet long and 45 feet wide. What is the perimeter of the pool?

$P = (2 \times l) + (2 \times w)$
$P = (2 \times \underline{?}) + (2 \times \underline{?})$
$P = \underline{?} + \underline{?}$
$P = \underline{?}$

The perimeter of the pool is $\underline{?}$ feet.

Use a formula or equation to solve. Show your work.

9. A park is shaped like a square with sides that are 4 kilometers long. What is the length of a bike path that goes around the outside border of the park?

10. Jessica's bedroom is 5 meters long and 3 meters wide. She puts a wallpaper border around the perimeter of the room near the ceiling. How long is the wallpaper border?

L E A R N

Formulas for Perimeter (B)

Solve with Perimeter Formulas

Use a formula, or equation, to find the perimeter. Show your work.
Write the answer with the correct unit.

1.

12 m

2 m

2. Charlie builds a sandbox for his grandson. It is a square with sides that are 5 feet long. What is the perimeter of the sandbox?

Read the problem and follow the directions.

3. Mr. Tunison is building a house. Part of the floor plan for the house is shown. Mr. Tunison is going to put carpet tape under the carpet around the sides of Room A and under the carpet around the hallway. How many feet of carpet tape does Mr. Tunison need? Show how to use formulas to find the answer.

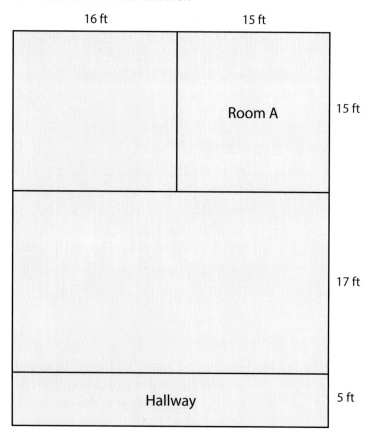

16 ft 15 ft

Room A 15 ft

17 ft

Hallway 5 ft

TRY IT

4. Find the missing measurements. Then find the perimeter. Explain how you got your answer.

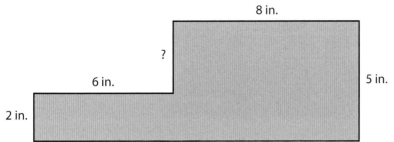

8 in.

?

6 in.

5 in.

2 in.

Choose the answer.

5. Mrs. Collins has two connected rectangular pens for her farm animals. The pens are shown. She wants to surround the pair of pens with new fence, but she does not want to put a new fence between the pens.

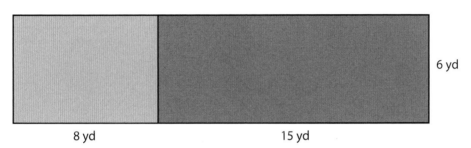

6 yd

8 yd

15 yd

What should Mrs. Collins do to find the total length of fencing needed to surround the pair of pens?

A. Add all the numbers shown in the drawing.

B. Find the perimeter of the smaller pen and then add 21.

C. Add the perimeters of the pens and then subtract 6.

D. Add the numbers shown in the drawing and then multiply by 2.

6. What is the perimeter of the swimming pool?

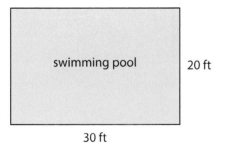

swimming pool

20 ft

30 ft

A. 50 ft

B. 100 ft

C. 200 ft

D. 600 ft

7. Ron installed wallpaper border around the top of his bedroom. If the rectangular bedroom measures 12 feet by 14 feet, how many feet of border did he use?

A. 26 ft

B. 48 ft

C. 52 ft

D. 56 ft

TRY IT

Choose the answer.

8. Tirey has a pool that measures 48 meters long and 15 meters wide. What is the perimeter of the pool?

   A. 63 m

   B. 96 m

   C. 116 m

   D. 126 m

9. Damon built a doghouse. The base was a perfect square that was 6 feet long on each side. What was the perimeter of the doghouse?

   A. 12 ft

   B. 18 ft

   C. 24 ft

   D. 36 ft

10. Manuella compared the perimeter of the figures.

Figure A

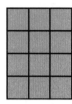

Figure B

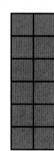

Figure C

Which sentence is true?

   A. The perimeter of Figure B is less than the perimeter of Figure A.

   B. The perimeter of Figure C is greater than the perimeter of Figure A.

   C. The perimeter of Figure A is less than the perimeter of Figure C.

   D. The perimeter of Figure A is equal to the perimeter of Figure C.

11. Which equation would **not** correctly calculate the perimeter of this rectangle?

5 cm

7 cm

   A. $P = 2 \times 5 + 7$

   B. $P = 7 + 5 + 7 + 5$

   C. $P = 2 \times (7 + 5)$

   D. $P = 2 \times 7 + 2 \times 5$

12. Which **two** equations could be used to calculate the perimeter of this square?

6 ft

   A. $P = 6 \times 6$

   B. $P = 6 + 6$

   C. $P = 6 \times 4$

   D. $P = 6 + 6 + 6 + 6$

TRY IT

13. Terrence compared the perimeters of the shaded figures.

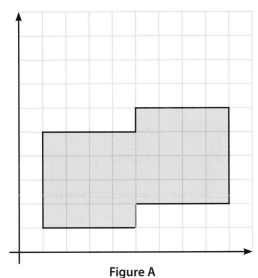

Figure A

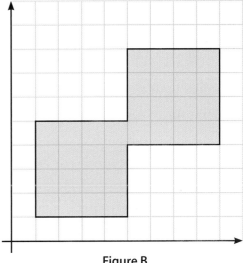

Figure B

Which sentence is true?

A. The perimeter of Figure A is greater than the perimeter of Figure B.

B. The perimeter of Figure A is less than the perimeter of Figure B.

14. Which statement about these rectangles is true?

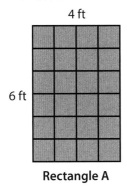

4 ft

6 ft

Rectangle A

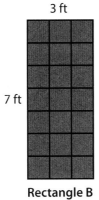

3 ft

7 ft

Rectangle B

A. The perimeter of Rectangle A is greater than the perimeter of Rectangle B.

B. The perimeter of Rectangle A is the same as the perimeter of Rectangle B.

T R Y   I T

Formulas for Area (A)

Solve with Area Formulas

Use a formula, or equation, to find the area. Show your work.

1.
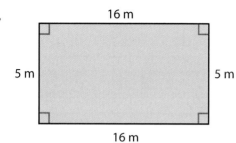

2.
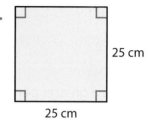

3. Find the area of a rectangle that is 21 yards long by 9 yards wide.

Solve.

4. Briana helps her mother make a quilt. The quilt is 6 feet wide and 12 feet long. What is the area of the quilt?

5. Use formulas to find the area of the compound figure. Show your work. Explain how you found your answer.

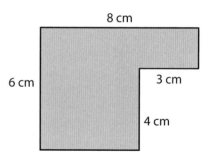

6. What is the area of this rectangle?

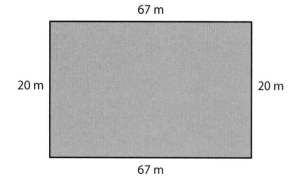

TRY IT

Choose the answer.

7. Shawn drew a diagram showing the dimensions of his closet and Emma's closet.

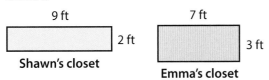

Shawn's closet

Emma's closet

Which statement about the closets is true?

A. Emma's closet has a greater perimeter and area.

B. Shawn's closet has a greater perimeter and area.

C. Emma's closet has a greater area but a smaller perimeter.

D. Shawn's closet has a greater area but a smaller perimeter.

8. Jennifer measured a rectangular garden in her backyard. The plot is shown.

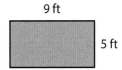

Which sentence gives the correct area and perimeter of Jennifer's garden?

A. The area is 14 ft^2 and the perimeter is 28 ft.

B. The area is 28 ft^2 and the perimeter is 45 ft.

C. The area is 45 ft^2 and the perimeter is 14 ft.

D. The area is 45 ft^2 and the perimeter is 28 ft.

9. Justice measured his rectangular vegetable garden.

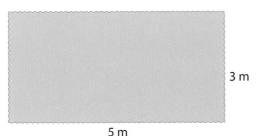

Which statement is true about the area and perimeter of Justice's garden?

A. The perimeter is 8 m and the area is 15 m^2.

B. The perimeter is 16 m and the area is 15 m^2.

C. The perimeter is 15 m and the area is 16 m^2.

D. The perimeter is 16 m and the area is 8 m^2.

10. On the grid, the shaded squares represent Nancy's closet floor.

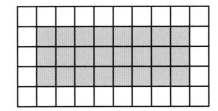

Nancy says the perimeter of the closet floor is 22 units and the area is 24 square units. Which sentence best explains if she is correct, and why or why not?

A. Yes, she is correct because the area of a floor is always greater than its perimeter.

B. Yes, she is correct because 24 is the number of squares needed to cover the surface, and 22 is the sum of all the sides.

C. No, she is incorrect because 22 is the number of squares needed to cover the surface, and 24 is the sum of all the sides.

D. No, she is incorrect because the perimeter of a floor is always greater than its area.

TRY IT

Choose the answer.

11. Which rectangle has an area smaller than the one shown?

3 cm

4 cm

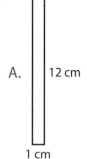

A. 12 cm

1 cm

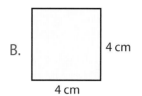

B. 4 cm

4 cm

C. 5 cm

3 cm

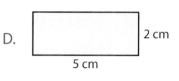

D. 2 cm

5 cm

12. What is the area of the figure shown?

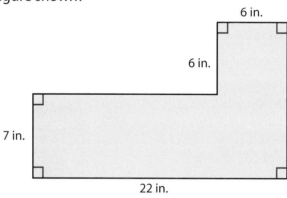

6 in.

6 in.

7 in.

22 in.

A. 252 in²   B. 190 in²   C. 174 in²   D. 154 in²

13. The dimensions of a rectangular tablecloth are shown.

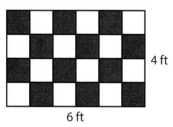

4 ft

6 ft

Which computation could be used to determine the area of the tablecloth?

A. Multiply 6 by 4.

B. Add 6 and 4.

C. Multiply 6 by 4, and then multiply by 2.

D. Add 6 and 4, and then multiply by 2.

14. Yolanda wants to water the grass in her rectangular backyard. Here is a diagram of the backyard.

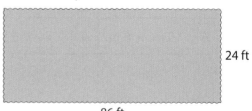

24 ft

86 ft

What is the area of Yolanda's backyard?

A. 220 ft²

B. 516 ft²

C. 1,884 ft²

D. 2,064 ft²

Formulas for Area (B)

Area of Complex Figures

Worked Examples

You can use area formulas to find the area of a complex figure. First you divide the figure into smaller rectangles or squares. Then you use formulas to find the area of the smaller figures. Next you find the sum of the areas.

PROBLEM Madeline wants to paste a flat piece of plastic to the front of the project display board shown. All angles are right angles. How many square inches of plastic does Madeline need?

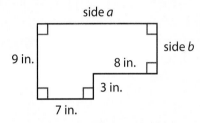

side a

side b

9 in.

8 in.

3 in.

7 in.

SOLUTION

1. Divide the figure into smaller rectangles or squares. Two ways to divide the figure are shown here. This solution is for the shaded figure on the left.

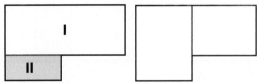

I

II

2. Use the given dimensions to find the dimensions that are not given.

3. Find the area of each rectangle.

Rectangle I	Rectangle II
$A = l \times w$	$A = l \times w$
$A = 15 \text{ in.} \times 6 \text{ in.}$	$A = 7 \text{ in.} \times 3 \text{ in.}$
$A = 90 \text{ in}^2$	$A = 21 \text{ in}^2$

side a
Together, the 7 in. side and the 8 in. side are the same length as side a.

- Add $7 + 8 = 15$. The length of side a is 15 in.
- Let 15 in. be the length of Rectangle I.

side b
The lengths of side b and the 3 in. side together are the same length as the 9 in. side. So 9 in. minus 3 in. is the length of side b.

- Subtract $9 - 3 = 6$. The length of side b is 6 in.
- Let 6 in. be the width of Rectangle I.

4. Add the areas of the two rectangles to find the total area.
$90 \text{ in}^2 + 21 \text{ in}^2 = 111 \text{ in}^2$

ANSWER Madeline needs 111 square inches of plastic to cover the front of the project display board.

L E A R N

Find the area. Show your work.

1.

1 ft

2 ft

4 ft   4 ft

Rectangle	Square
$A = ? \times ?$	$A = ? \times ?$
$A = ? \times ?$	$A = ? \times ?$
$A = ?$	$A = ?$

Total area $= ?$ ft^2 $+ ?$ ft^2 $= ?$ ft^2

2. The pyramid El Castillo stands in the Yucatan peninsula of Mexico. It has a square base with four staircases that jut out, one on each side. Joe drew an outline of a complex figure like the El Castillo pyramid. The dimensions are approximate. Use Joe's diagram to find the approximate total area that the base of the pyramid covers.

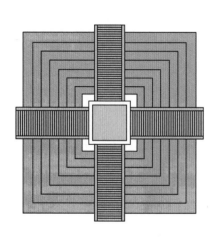

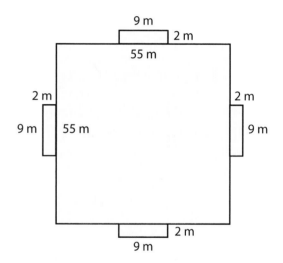

Square	Rectangle
$A = ? \times ?$	$A = ? \times ?$
$A = ?$	$A = ?$

The total area $= ?$ m^2 $+(4 \times ?$ m$^2)$

$= ?$ m^2 $+ ?$ m^2

$= ?$ m^2

Formulas for Area (B)

Interpret and Use Formulas

Find the perimeter and area of the figure. Explain how you found your answer.

1.

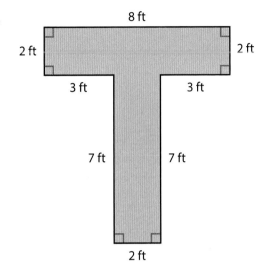

8 ft
2 ft
2 ft
3 ft
3 ft
7 ft
7 ft
2 ft

2.

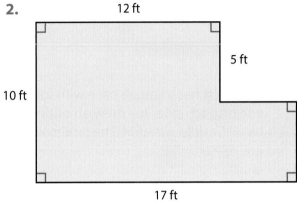

12 ft
5 ft
10 ft
17 ft

Use Problems 1 and 2 to solve.

3. Which has the greater area?

4. Which has the lesser perimeter?

Solve. Explain how you found your answer.

5. The plastic flag on the mailbox at Janine's house is shown. Find the area of the entire figure.

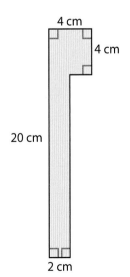

4 cm
4 cm
20 cm
2 cm

Solve.

6. What is the area of a rectangular field that is 25 meters long and 15 meters wide?

7. What is the area of a square if one side is 14 centimeters long?

TRY IT

Choose the answer.

8. A rectangle is 32 meters long and 4 meters wide. Which equation represents the area (*A*) of the rectangle?

   A. $A = 32 \times 4$

   B. $32 = (4 \times A) \times 4$

   C. $32 = A \times 4$

   D. $A = (2 \times 4) + (2 \times 32)$

9. Which rectangle has an area greater than the one shown?

   15 m
   2 m

   A.
   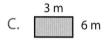
   7 m
   4 m

   B.
   13 m
   3 m

   C.
   3 m
   6 m

   D.
   16 m
   1 m

10. Which figure has an area greater than the one shown?

    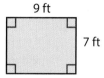
    9 ft
    7 ft

    A.
    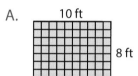
    10 ft
    8 ft

    B.
    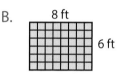
    8 ft
    6 ft

    C.
    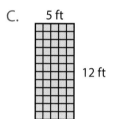
    5 ft
    12 ft

    D.
    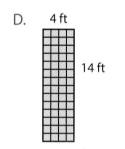
    4 ft
    14 ft

11. What is the area of the figure?

    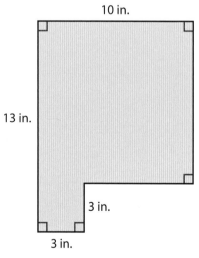
    10 in.
    13 in.
    3 in.
    3 in.

    A. 109 in²

    B. 100 in²

    C. 90 in²

    D. 46 in²

12. What is the area of the figure?

    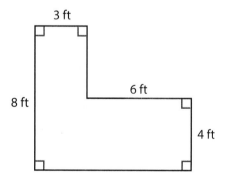
    3 ft
    8 ft
    6 ft
    4 ft

    A. 60 ft²

    B. 50 ft²

    C. 48 ft²

    D. 24 ft²

TRY IT

13. What is the area of the figure?

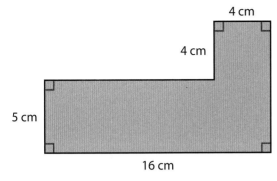

A. 80 cm²

B. 84 cm²

C. 88 cm²

D. 96 cm²

14. What is the area of the figure?

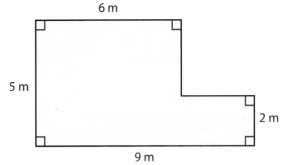

A. 36 m²

B. 30 m²

C. 12 m²

D. 9 m²

15. Mr. McBean is fencing a rectangular pasture for his horses. What is the area of the pasture that will be used for Mr. McBean's horses?

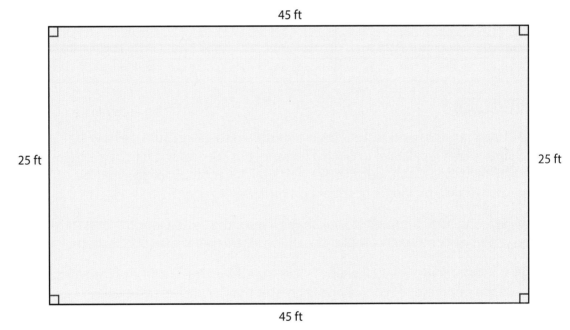

A. 140 ft²

B. 140 yd²

C. 1,125 ft²

D. 1,125 yd²

T R Y   I T

Compare Area and Perimeter

Same Perimeter, Different Areas

Worked Examples

You can use 1-inch square tiles to build rectangles or squares with the same perimeter but different areas. You can also use 1-inch grid paper to draw rectangles or squares with the same perimeter but different areas. Then you can enter your data in a table to compare the areas of these shapes.

PROBLEM Build or draw rectangles or squares, each with a perimeter of 14 inches. Use the table to help you write the dimensions of each shape. Then write the area of each shape.

Same Perimeter, Different Areas				
Name of shape	Length (*l*)	Width (*w*)	Area (*A*)	Perimeter (*P*)
Shape 1	$l = ?$ in.	$w = ?$ in.	$A = ?$ in^2	$P = 14$ in.
Shape 2	$l = ?$ in.	$w = ?$ in.	$A = ?$ in^2	$P = 14$ in.
Shape 3	$l = ?$ in.	$w = ?$ in.	$A = ?$ in^2	$P = 14$ in.

SOLUTION

1 Use the guess-and-test method of problem solving. Estimate how many tiles it will take to build a rectangle or square that has a perimeter of 14 inches. Count out the tiles and build a rectangle or square. You can also draw a rectangle or square on grid paper.

2 Starting at one corner of your shape, count the 1-inch lengths that form a border completely around the shape, or the perimeter of the shape.

3 If the perimeter of your shape is less than 14 inches, add 1 or more tiles. If the perimeter of your shape is greater than 14 inches, take away 1 or more tiles. Continue this process until you build a rectangle or square with a perimeter of 14 inches.

4 Record the dimensions of your first shape.

5 Count the 1-inch square tiles that make up the shape, or the area of the shape. You may also use the formula $A = l \times w$ or the formula $A = s \times s$. Record the area of the shape.

6 Continue to build rectangles that each have a 14-inch perimeter. The dimensions must be different for each shape.

Record the dimensions and areas of each new shape, but do not record a shape twice. For example, a 5-inch by 2-inch rectangle should not also be recorded as a 2-inch by 5-inch rectangle.

ANSWER

Same Perimeter, Different Areas				
Name of shape	Length (*l*)	Width (*w*)	Area (*A*)	Perimeter (*P*)
Shape 1	*l* = 6 in.	*w* = 1 in.	*A* = 6 in²	*P* = 14 in.
Shape 2	*l* = 5 in.	*w* = 2 in.	*A* = 10 in²	*P* = 14 in.
Shape 3	*l* = 4 in.	*w* = 3 in.	*A* = 12 in²	*P* = 14 in.

Use 1-inch square tiles or 1-inch grid paper to solve the problem.

1. Build or draw rectangles or squares, each with a perimeter of 16 inches. Use the table to record the dimensions of each shape. Then record the area of each shape.

Same Perimeter, Different Areas				
Name of shape	Length (*l*)	Width (*w*)	Area (*A*)	Perimeter (*P*)
Shape 1	*l* = ? in.	*w* = ? in.	*A* = ? in²	*P* = 16 in.
Shape 2	*l* = ? in.	*w* = ? in.	*A* = ? in²	*P* = 16 in.
Shape 3	*l* = ? in.	*w* = ? in.	*A* = ? in²	*P* = 16 in.
Shape 4	*s* = ? in.	*s* = ? in.	*A* = ? in²	*P* = 16 in.

2. Build or draw rectangles or squares, each with a perimeter of 8 inches. Use the table to record the dimensions of each shape. Then record the area of each shape.

Same Perimeter, Different Areas				
Name of shape	Length (*l*)	Width (*w*)	Area (*A*)	Perimeter (*P*)
Shape 1	*l* = ? in.	*w* = ? in.	*A* = ? in²	*P* = 8 in.
Shape 2	*s* = ? in.	*s* = ? in.	*A* = ? in²	*P* = 8 in.

Use this table to answer Problems 3 and 4.

Rectangles: Same Perimeter, Different Areas			
Name of shape	Length (*l*)	Width (*w*)	Perimeter (*P*)
Shape 1	9 in.	1 in.	20 in.
Shape 2	8 in.	2 in.	20 in.
Shape 3	7 in.	3 in.	20 in.
Shape 4	6 in.	4 in.	20 in.
Shape 5	5 in.	5 in.	20 in.

3. Which shape has an area of 24 square inches? Use an area formula to explain your answer.

4. The table shows the dimensions of four rectangles and one square that each have a perimeter of 20 inches. Could you use 1-inch square tiles to build a square with a perimeter of 18 inches? Explain your answer.

Solve.

5. A 3-centimeter by 8-centimeter mailing label has a perimeter of 22 centimeters and an area of 24 square centimeters. What are the dimensions of another label that has the same perimeter but a different area?

6. Mr. Liska decides to buy one of the banners listed in the table. Each has a perimeter of 18 feet. Which banner should Mr. Liska choose if he wants one with the greatest area? Explain your answer.

Color of banner	Length (*l*)	Width (*w*)	Perimeter (*P*)
yellow	7 ft	2 ft	18 ft
purple	5 ft	4 ft	18 ft
orange	8 ft	1 ft	18 ft
pink	6 ft	3 ft	18 ft

LEARN

Compare Area and Perimeter

Same Area, Different Perimeters

Worked Examples

You can use 1-inch square tiles to build rectangles or squares with the same area but different perimeters. You can also use 1-inch grid paper to draw the rectangles or squares with the same area but different perimeters. Then you can enter your data in a table to compare the perimeters of these shapes.

PROBLEM Build or draw rectangles or squares, each with an area of 16 square inches. Use the table to record the dimensions of each shape. Then record the perimeter of each shape.

Same Area, Different Perimeters				
Name of shape	**Length (*l*)**	**Width (*w*)**	**Perimeter (*P*)**	**Area (*A*)**
Shape 1	$l = ?$ in.	$w = ?$ in.	$P = ?$ in.	$A = 16$ in^2
Shape 2	$l = ?$ in.	$w = ?$ in.	$P = ?$ in.	$A = 16$ in^2
Shape 3	$s = ?$ in.	$s = ?$ in.	$P = ?$ in.	$A = 16$ in^2

SOLUTION

1 Count out 16 tiles or prepare to draw on grid paper. Build or draw a rectangle that has an area of 16 square inches.

2 Use the table to record the rectangle's dimensions. Then starting at one corner of the rectangle, count the 1-inch lengths that form a border completely around the shape, or the perimeter of the shape. You may also use a perimeter formula, such as $P = 2 \times (l + w)$. Record the perimeter of your rectangle.

3 Build or draw a second rectangle with an area of 16 square inches. Do not record a shape twice. For example, an 8-inch by 2-inch rectangle should not also be recorded as a 2-inch by 8-inch rectangle. Record the dimensions and perimeter of the second rectangle.

4 Build or draw a square with an area of 16 square inches. Record the dimensions and perimeter of the square.

LEARN

Same Area, Different Perimeters				
Name of shape	Length (*l*)	Width (*w*)	Perimeter (*P*)	Area (*A*)
Shape 1	16 in.	1 in.	34 in.	$A = 16$ in²
Shape 2	8 in.	2 in.	20 in.	$A = 16$ in²
Shape 3	4 in.	4 in.	16 in.	$A = 16$ in²

Use 1-inch square tiles or 1-inch grid paper to solve the problem.

1. Build or draw rectangles, each with an area of 20 square inches. Use the table to record the dimensions of each shape. Then record the perimeter of each shape.

Same Area, Different Perimeters				
Name of rectangle	Length (*l*)	Width (*w*)	Perimeter (*P*)	Area (*A*)
Rectangle 1	$l = ?$ in.	$w = ?$ in.	$P = ?$ in.	$A = 20$ in²
Rectangle 2	$l = ?$ in.	$w = ?$ in.	$P = ?$ in.	$A = 20$ in²
Rectangle 3	$l = ?$ in.	$w = ?$ in.	$P = ?$ in.	$A = 20$ in²

2. Build or draw a rectangle and a square, each with an area of 25 square inches. Use the table to record the dimensions of each shape. Then record the perimeter of each shape.

Same Area, Different Perimeters				
Name of shape	Length (*l*)	Width (*w*)	Perimeter (*P*)	Area (*A*)
Shape 1	$l = ?$ in.	$w = ?$ in.	$P = ?$ in.	$A = 25$ in²
Shape 2	$s = ?$ in.	$s = ?$ in.	$P = ?$ in.	$A = 25$ in²

LEARN

Use this table to answer Problems 3 and 4.

Rectangles: Same Area, Different Perimeters			
Name of rectangle	Length (*l*)	Width (*w*)	Area (*A*)
Rectangle 1	8 in.	6 in.	48 in²
Rectangle 2	12 in.	4 in.	48 in²
Rectangle 3	24 in.	2 in.	48 in²
Rectangle 4	48 in.	1 in.	48 in²

3. Which rectangle has a perimeter of 52 inches? Use a perimeter formula to explain your answer.

4. Which rectangle has the greatest perimeter? Use a perimeter formula to explain your answer.

Solve.

5. Alexander has a garden that is 5 yards by 6 yards. He wants to make another garden with the same area but different dimensions. Should he make a garden that is 10 yards by 3 yards, or should he make one that is 4 yards by 6 yards?

6. Rosa has two rectangular rugs in her house. The two rugs have the same area but different perimeters. Which of the following rugs could belong to Rosa? Explain your answer.

Color of rug	Length (*l*)	Width (*w*)
blue	5 ft	4 ft
red	9 ft	2 ft
green	8 ft	2 ft
black	6 ft	3 ft

LEARN

Compare Area and Perimeter

Area and Perimeter Problems

Answer the question.

1. Do these shapes have the same area or the same perimeter?

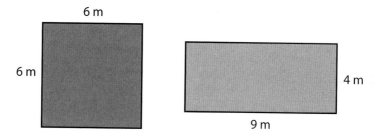

2. How are these rectangles alike and different in terms of their perimeters and areas?

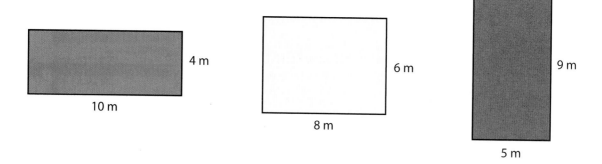

Use this rectangle to answer Problems 3 and 4.

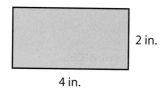

3. Draw and label a shape that has the same perimeter but a different area.

4. Draw and label a shape that has the same area but a different perimeter.

TRY IT

Choose the answer.

5. Each rectangle and square with the dimensions listed has a perimeter of 16 inches. Which rectangle has an area of 12 square inches?

   A. 6 in. by 2 in.

   B. 5 in. by 3 in.

   C. 4 in. by 4 in.

   D. 7 in. by 1 in.

6. Which of the following statements is true about these rectangles?

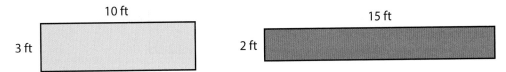

10 ft

3 ft

15 ft

2 ft

   A. They have the same area but different perimeters.

   B. They have the same perimeter but different areas.

   C. They have different areas and perimeters.

   D. They have the same areas and perimeters.

7. Which of the following statements is true about these rectangles?

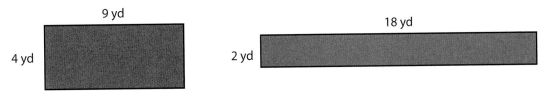

9 yd

4 yd

18 yd

2 yd

   A. They have different areas and perimeters.

   B. They have the same area but different perimeters.

   C. They have the same areas and perimeters.

   D. They have the same perimeter but different areas.

8. The listed options give the dimensions of different rectangles with an area of 60 square inches.

   Which dimensions will result in the greatest perimeter?

   A. 20 in. by 3 in.

   B. 10 in. by 6 in.

   C. 15 in. by 4 in.

   D. 30 in. by 2 in.

TRY IT

Choose the answer.

9. A rectangle with a length of 7 feet and a width of 4 feet has an area of 28 square feet and a perimeter of 22 feet.

   Which **two** rectangles have dimensions that give the same area as this rectangle but different perimeters?

   A. 2 ft by 14 ft

   B. 28 ft by 1 ft

   C. 5 ft by 6 ft

   D. 8 ft by 3 ft

10. Each option describes a rectangle with an area of 24 square centimeters.

    Which dimensions describe a rectangle with a perimeter of 28 centimeters?

    A. 1 cm by 24 cm

    B. 2 cm by 12 cm

    C. 3 cm by 8 cm

    D. 4 cm by 6 cm

11. This square and this rectangle have equal perimeters.

    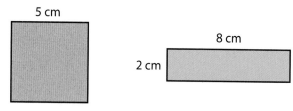

    5 cm

    8 cm

    2 cm

    Based on this information, which statement is true?

    A. The figures are both squares.

    B. The figures have different areas.

    C. The figures have the same dimensions.

    D. The figures have different angle measures.

12. Which of the following statements is true about these rectangles?

    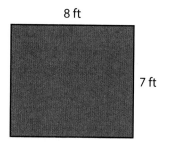

    8 ft

    7 ft

    10 ft

    5 ft

    A. They have different perimeters and different areas.

    B. They have different areas but the same perimeter.

    C. They have the same perimeter and the same area.

    D. They have the same area but different perimeters.

13. Each shape has a perimeter of 26 feet. Which shape has the greatest area?

A.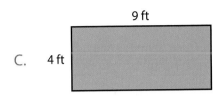
10 ft
3 ft

B.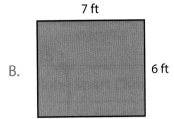
7 ft
6 ft

C.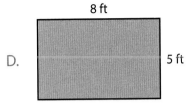
9 ft
4 ft

D.
8 ft
5 ft

14. This rectangle has a perimeter of 40 centimeters and an area of 84 square centimeters.

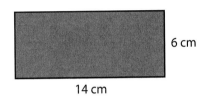

6 cm

14 cm

Which rectangle also has a perimeter of 40 centimeters but has a different area?

A. 12 cm by 8 cm

B. 25 cm by 15 cm

C. 10 cm by 4 cm

D. 42 cm by 2 cm

TRY IT

Worked Examples

You can use the problem-solving plan to solve story problems involving area. One way to solve a multistep area problem is to draw a diagram to help you break the problem into simpler parts.

PROBLEM Mr. Nolan wants to plant a 2-foot-wide flower border around part of his yard. He drew this diagram to show how it should look. How many square feet of flower border will Mr. Noland need to plant?

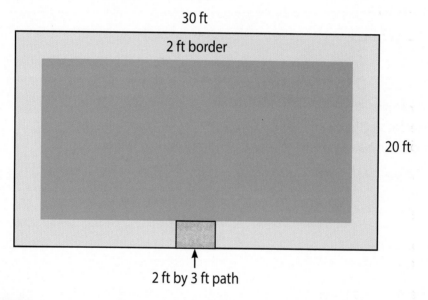

30 ft

2 ft border

20 ft

2 ft by 3 ft path

SOLUTION

UNDERSTAND THE PROBLEM You need to know how many total square feet of flower border Mr. Nolan needs to plant.

DEVISE A PLAN Use the diagram to break the problem into simpler parts.

1 Draw lines to divide the diagram into several rectangles that don't overlap.

2 Find how many square feet are in the top of the border.

3 Find how many square feet are in the bottom of the border.

4 Find how many square feet are in the two sides of the border.

5 Write a number sentence to find the total number of square feet Mr. Nolan needs to plant.

CARRY OUT THE PLAN

1 One way to divide the diagram into several rectangles that don't overlap is shown below.

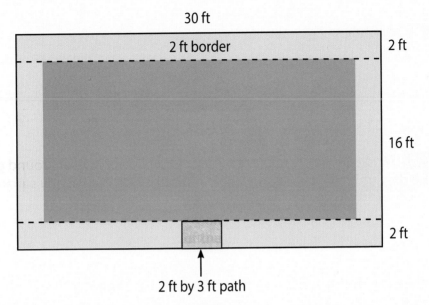

30 ft

2 ft border

2 ft

16 ft

2 ft

2 ft by 3 ft path

2 Use the formula for finding area to find the areas of each of the rectangles. To find the area of the top border, multiply the length by the width: $30 \times 2 = 60$ square feet.

3 The area of the bottom of the border is the same as the area of the top of the border minus the area of the path. The area of the path is $2 \times 3 = 6$ square feet, so the area of the bottom border is $60 - 6 = 54$ square feet.

4 The area of a side of the border is $16 \times 2 = 32$ square feet. The total area of the two sides of the border is $32 \times 2 = 64$ square feet.

5 To find the total area, add the areas of the top, bottom, and side borders: $60 + 54 + 64 = 178$ square feet.

LOOK BACK Make sure you've answered the question that was asked. Estimate the answer, about 200 square feet ($120 \text{ ft}^2 + 80 \text{ ft}^2 = 200 \text{ ft}^2$). Since 178 square feet is close to the estimate of 200 square feet, the answer makes sense.

ANSWER Mr. Nolan needs to plant 178 square feet of flower border.

LEARN

Solve.

1. Jack bought a new rug for his bedroom. The width of the border around the rug is 2 feet. The diagram shows how the rug looks in Jack's bedroom.

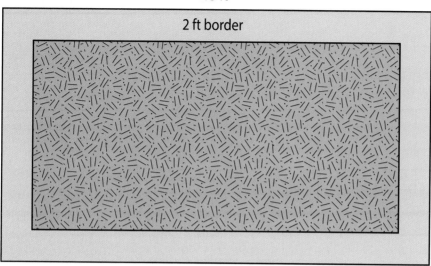

15 ft

2 ft border

12 ft

(a) What are the length and the width of the rug Jack bought? Explain.

(b) How many square feet of the floor are left uncovered? Explain.

2. Mia is covering a 12-inch-square board with 1-inch-square tiles. She uses red tiles to make a 3-inch by 3-inch square in each corner. She covers the rest of the board with blue tiles. How many more blue tiles than red tiles will Mia use? Explain.

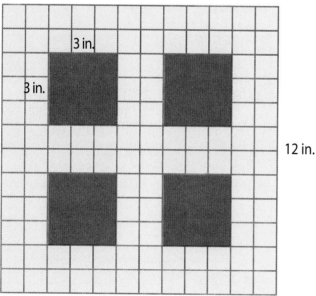

12 in.

3 in.

3 in.

12 in.

LEARN

Explain Multistep Area Problems

Solve.

1. Rosa wants to buy a new rug for her room. The diagram shows the rug that she now has in her room.

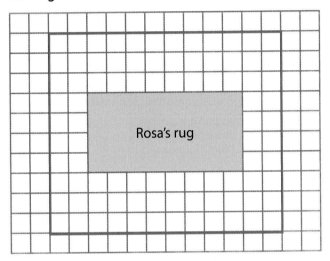

   Rosa's rug

   Rosa finds two rectangular rugs she likes. Each rug is 8 square feet larger than the rug she has now. Each rug has a different perimeter. Each side is greater than 2 feet.

   (a) What are the perimeters of the two rugs Rosa likes? Explain how you found the answer.

   (b) How many square feet of Rosa's room will **not** be covered by the rug she buys? Explain how you found the answer.

2. Jerrod wants to cover his work table with tiles. He wants to cover an area 32 inches long by 20 inches wide. He finds two different sizes of tiles that he likes.

   (a) Draw a diagram to show how many 4 in. by 4 in. tiles Jerrod needs to cover his work table. How many does he need?

   (b) Draw a diagram to show how many 2 in. by 4 in. tiles Jerrod needs to cover his work table. How many does he need?

   (c) Use your answers to Parts (a) and (b) to show how many more 2 in. by 4 in. tiles than 4 in. by 4 in. tiles it will take to cover the table. Explain.

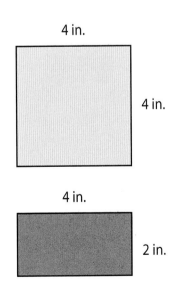

4 in.

4 in.

4 in.

2 in.

T R Y   I T

Solve.

3. Harold wants to paint a 2-inch-wide border around the edge of a poster he is making. He drew this diagram to show how it should look.

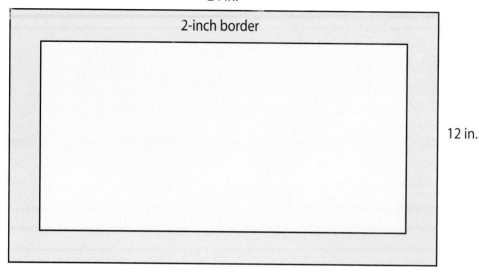

24 in.

2-inch border

12 in.

(a) How many square inches of border will Harold paint?
   Describe the plan you used for solving the problem.

(b) How many square inches of poster will be left unpainted?
   Explain how you found the answer.

Think Like a Mathematician Self-Check

4. State the actions and thinking you used during this lesson as a math learner.

Math Thinking and Actions
I made sense of problems by • Explaining to myself what a problem means and what it asks for • Using drawings or diagrams to represent a problem I was solving
I explained my math thinking clearly.
I tried out new ways to check if an answer is reasonable.
Other

TRY IT